Streets
and Roads

by WILLIAM S. GRAY *and* MAY HILL ARBUTHNOT

BASIC READERS: CURRICULUM FOUNDATION SERIES

THE 1946-47 EDITION

Scott, Foresman and Company

CHICAGO   ATLANTA   DALLAS   NEW YORK

On City Streets

Along Country Roads

On the Road to Story-Land

Animals in Town and Country

On the Roads of Long Ago

On
City Streets

John and the Robins

Park Street was a very busy street in a very big city.

Swish, swish went the automobiles all day long and all night long. Honk, honk went the buses. Trip-trap, trip-trap, trip-trap went the people's feet on the sidewalks.

All along the street there were tall buildings.

At one end of the street there was a pretty green park, and so the street was named Park Street.

John and Susan Hall and their little brother Tommy lived in one of the tall buildings on the street. It was called the Park Street Building. Many other people lived there, too.

One morning the three Hall children came hurrying out of the front door.

Tim, the doorman, smiled one of his big smiles as he held it open for them.

"I know what you want," he said. "You want to look at the baby robins that live in our tree."

Right in front of the building stood a tree. And in that tree a mother robin and a father robin had their nest.

At first there had been three little blue eggs in the nest, and now there were three baby robins.

"Look!" cried Susan. "The mother robin is bringing food again. Her babies seem to be hungry all the time. It's no wonder they are growing so fast."

"Yes, they are getting big," said Tim. "I believe they will soon try to fly."

And Tim was right, for just then one baby robin did try to fly.

Down from the tree it came. It didn't really fly, and it didn't really fall. It just came down. Then, hippety-hop, it went right out into the street.

"Oh, Tim," shouted John, "the robin will be run over by an automobile!"

"I'll try to save it," said Tim, and in half a second he was out in the street.

Honk, honk went the automobiles. Honk, honk went the big buses, too.

But the big buses didn't frighten Tim.

"Stop!" he shouted, as he held up his hand.

The cars and the buses stopped right where they were.

People looked out of the buses to see what was the matter. The people on the sidewalks looked, too. Everybody wondered what was the matter.

Tim reached down quickly to pick up
the little bird, but it was faster than
he was. In half a second it hopped
under a car. Tim reached for it, but
it hopped under another car.

"Peep, peep," said the little bird.

Tim ran over and reached under that
car, but then the robin hopped under
one of the buses. This time Tim got
hold of the bird with both hands.

"Ha!" he cried. "Now I have you."

"Hurrah for Tim!" cried John.

"Hurrah for Tim!" cried everybody.

Tim took the robin back to the walk,
and the cars and buses started again.

Tim said, "The robin isn't hurt at all. But how can we take care of it?"

"Oh," said John, "can't you put it back in the nest?"

"Yes," answered Tim, "but I don't believe it would be safe if I did. It was trying to fly, and it will try again."

"Oh, dear!" cried Susan. "Then it might hop into the street again and be run over by an automobile."

"I know a way to take care of the robin," said John. "Just wait half a minute." And he ran into the building.

When he came back, he held something in his hand.

"The baby robins can live in this," he said. "Then they can't fall into the street. They will be safe."

"That's just what we need," cried Tim. "We'll put the baby robins in it and keep them safe."

John had a big old bird cage in his hand. While John held the cage, Tim put the baby robin in it.

"We'll tie the cage in the tree," said Tim. "We need string and a ladder."

"I'll be your helper," said Tommy. "I'll get string, but I can't get a ladder."

"I'll get the ladder," said Tim.

Tommy brought the string, and Tim brought the ladder. Then he took the cage and climbed up.

The old birds flew around and made a lot of noise. Tweet! Tweet! They were afraid Tim would hurt their baby.

Tim tied the cage to a branch and put the other little birds in it.

As soon as Tim was halfway down the ladder, the old birds flew toward the cage. "Tweet, tweet!" they cried.

Susan felt sorry for the big robins. "How frightened they are!" she said. "They don't like the cage."

"Never mind," said Tim, taking away the ladder. "They will get used to it."

And they did. In a few minutes they were not frightened any more. They began to carry food to their babies.

The three Hall children looked up at the birds and laughed. It was funny to see robins living in a cage in a tree.

The robins stayed in the cage for a few days. They were safe there.

One day Tim said to the Hall children, "Maybe the robins are big enough to fly now. Why don't you carry them to the park and let them go?"

Tim got a ladder and took the cage down from the tree.

The young robins were frightened and kept hopping around in the cage and making sad little cries. Tw-ee-t, tw-ee-t!

On the way to the park the children took turns carrying the cage.

When they reached the park, John put the cage on the ground and opened it.

Then the young robins hopped out. They lifted their wings and moved them up and down. At last they flew away.

"Hurrah! Hurrah!" cried John. "The robins don't need a cage any more because now they can really fly."

Susan's Birthday Picnic

"Oh, Tim!" cried Susan. "Today is my birthday, and I'm eight years old. Look at all my presents."

She felt very happy as she showed Tim her new roller skates, a story book, and a paint box with eight colors in it.

"And see my new umbrella," she said. "It has pictures of kittens on it."

"Well," said Tim with a smile, "you must be having a happy birthday."

"Oh, yes!" cried Susan. "And now we are going to the country for a picnic."

She skipped off to the car, and the Hall family started on the picnic.

They rode along, and soon they were out in the country.

They rode past farmhouses with great big barns and past many green fields.

"I know just the place for Susan's birthday picnic," said Father. "It's in a beautiful forest. And there is a pond where Tommy can sail his boat."

"Hurrah!" cried Tommy. "I'll have a place to sail my boat."

"Where is this place?" asked Susan.

Father answered, "You will soon see. We turn to the right at the very next filling station."

When they came to the next filling station, they started to turn to the right.

But they couldn't turn. The road was closed, and there was a sign with big letters on it. "Detour," it said.

"I didn't know this road had been closed," said Father. "This detour won't take us to the place I was talking about. But never mind. We'll take the detour anyway and see if we can find a nice cool place for a picnic."

So they took the detour. They rode past a farmhouse with a lot of beehives in the yard and past a field where there were horses and cows and one little calf.

Soon Mrs. Hall cried, "Let's stop. I see a nice cool place for our picnic."

Mr. Hall stopped the automobile, and everybody got out. Then John opened a gate that was near the road, and ran toward a grove of oak trees.

But in a minute John stopped and waited for the others.

"Look at that!" he called.

He pointed to a sign on an oak tree.

Susan read the sign out loud. "Oh, dear!" she cried. "We can't have my birthday picnic here. And this is such a nice place." She felt a little sad.

"Never mind," said Father. "We'll go somewhere else. We'll find a better place."

Everybody got into the car, and Father drove off.

They rode on, and after a while they saw a nice place near a bridge. There was a grove of maple trees by the river, and wild roses were growing in the sun.

Father said, "That grove looks like a pleasant place. I'll stop here."

He stopped, and they all got out.

Tommy skipped ahead. He passed the wild roses, but when he got near the maple grove, he stopped.

"I see a sign," he called. "It has big letters on it. What does it say?"

"I'll read it to you," said Susan. She read the sign with the big letters on it.

NO PICNICS HERE

"We can't stay here," said Father. "But never mind. We'll go somewhere else. We'll find a better place."

They got in, and Father drove off.

They rode on and on, but they didn't find a good place for a picnic. And soon they all felt very hot and hungry.

At last Tommy said, "I don't think I can wait much longer for my dinner."

"Oh, dear!" said Susan. "Can't we find any place for our picnic?"

Then Father said, "I've just thought of a place where we can have our picnic. It has trees and grass and a pond with fish in it. Tommy can sail his boat there. It's a surprise place."

He drove straight ahead for a while.

Then he told the children, "Now shut your eyes and keep them shut. When we get to the surprise place, I'll count slowly up to eight. When I say eight, you may open your eyes."

The children closed their eyes and kept them closed. It was hard not to look, but they didn't open their eyes once.

At last Father stopped the car and began to count.

When he called, "Eight," the children opened their eyes and looked out of the windows. They saw trees and green grass and a pond where Tommy could sail his boat.

But when they got out of the car, Tommy saw a sign with big letters on it.

"Does it say 'No picnics'?" he asked.

"No, it doesn't," answered Susan, and she read the sign out loud.

PICNICS HERE

John ran ahead of the others and found
a table. Then Susan helped Mother put
the picnic dinner on the table.

All at once John shouted, "See that
tall building over there! Isn't that the
Park Street Building? Why, look! We
are in the park at the end of our own
street!"

"What a joke on us!" laughed Susan.
"We made a great big detour to find a
place for our picnic. And all the time
our own park was the very best place!"

The Big, Long Honk

One day Tommy was riding in the front seat of the car with his father.

"Please let me honk the horn," he said, as they passed a car. "Please!"

"All right," answered his father.

John and Susan were in the back seat. They laughed at their little brother because he always wanted to honk the horn.

Tommy wanted to honk whenever they passed buses or cars or bicycles. And he wanted to honk at every corner, too.

Soon Father drove up to a big brick building and slowed down. Just then the automobile ahead of him began to back out into the street.

"That car might bump into us," said Tommy. And he honked long and loud.

"Stop, Tommy," said Father. "Just a little, short honk is enough."

"All right," answered Tommy. "But I like big, long honks better."

Father stopped the car and got out. "I have to do an errand," he said. "I'm going to buy some flour and eggs and milk for Mother. Tommy, you stay here with John and Susan."

"All right," answered Tommy, sliding over toward the wheel. "Shall I honk the horn while you do the errand?"

Father had gone into the grocery store and didn't hear him. But Susan cried, "No! No! Don't honk the horn."

"Just forget about the horn," said John. "Look at those boys passing us. They are riding on red bicycles."

Tommy turned to look at the boys on red bicycles, and his arm rested on the wheel. Honk, honk, honk went the horn.

Quickly Tommy lifted his arm from the wheel, but the horn didn't stop.

"Tommy!" cried Susan. "Quit making that awful noise. Don't honk the horn."

"I'm not honking it," said Tommy. "Nobody is honking it."

He held up his hands to show that he wasn't touching the wheel. But the awful noise still kept on, because the horn was stuck.

Then John climbed into the front seat. He pushed and pounded, but he couldn't make the honking stop, no matter how hard he pounded.

Soon there was a crowd of people on the walk beside the car.

"Just listen to that awful noise!" cried a tall man in the crowd. "And look at that big boy behind the wheel. He's honking the horn."

Then Tommy began to laugh. "People think you are honking the horn," he said to John.

John climbed into the back seat again.

Then Tommy turned around with a smile. "This is a long honk," he said.

And it was a long honk. It was the longest and loudest honk that Tommy had ever heard.

Dogs barked, and babies cried. People banged their windows shut. Nobody but Tommy liked the big, long honk.

The crowd near the car got bigger. Soon the walk was filled with people.

A policeman with a silver star on his blue coat came hurrying through the crowd. He looked at Tommy and said in a gruff voice, "What do you mean by making such a noise? Quit honking that horn."

"I'm not honking it," cried Tommy. "Nobody is honking it. It started a few minutes ago, and now it won't stop. It's stuck. I think this is fun."

Mr. Hall heard the awful noise and came hurrying out of the grocery store. He pushed his way through the crowd.

"Tommy!" he cried. "Stop honking that horn. Stop this minute!"

"I'm not honking it," said Tommy. "Nobody is honking it. It's stuck."

The storekeeper in his white apron came running out. He was carrying the big bag of groceries that Mr. Hall had bought. In his hurry Mr. Hall had left the flour, eggs, and milk in the store.

Father tried to stop the horn by giving the wheel a little tap. Then he gave it a hard knock. He hammered it with his hand. Bumpety-bump-bump! He pounded and pounded.

But the horn was stuck, and it kept on honking. The noise was terrible.

"I'm sorry," Father told the policeman. "I can't make the horn stop."

Just then a man came running from a filling station on the corner. He said, "Perhaps I can fix your horn."

So the man from the filling station looked at the engine. Then he moved something, and the honking stopped. Suddenly the street seemed very quiet.

"My!" said Father. "I'm glad that awful noise has stopped."

"I'm not," laughed Tommy. "I liked it. It was a big, long honk. A big, long honk at last."

Lost and Found

One day Nancy Fox came to live in the Park Street Building. She had just moved to the city from a small village.

Soon Nancy and Susan were friends. They went to school together every day, and after school they went to the park on their roller skates or bicycles.

One Saturday they went downtown together. They went to a big store with Mrs. Hall and John.

John ran ahead of his mother and the
two girls.

"Let's go to the third floor and look
at the toys," he called. "Come on!
This elevator will take us up."

They all got in, and the elevator man
shut the door and started the elevator.

Up it went, past the second floor.
When the elevator came to the third
floor, it stopped, and Mrs. Hall and the
children got out.

"Let's look at dolls," said Nancy.

"I don't want to look at dolls," said John. "I want to slide on the big slide and look at sailboats and airplanes and trains. The last time I was here, I saw a silver train with a toy station."

"All right, John," said his mother. "You look at airplanes and sailboats and trains, while the girls look at dolls.

"I am going to buy some shoes and an umbrella.

"In half an hour we'll all meet under the big clock by these elevators."

"All right," said the children, and they started off.

Susan and Nancy passed the toy trains and airplanes and wagons, and then they came to the dolls. There were hundreds of dolls. Hundreds and hundreds!

Dolls that could close their eyes and go to sleep. Dolls that could say ma-ma. Clown dolls and policeman dolls. And even a little boy doll with a drum.

There was a fairy doll with dozens of silver stars on her dress and silver stars in her hair. Nancy stopped and looked at the fairy doll for a long time.

"Oh, Susan!" she cried at last. "Look at this doll with the silver stars."

Susan didn't answer. She wasn't there. Nancy walked around looking for her.

Soon she came to some stairs. But what queer stairs they were. They were moving! They were going up, up, up!

People stood on the stairs and rode up to the next floor.

Nancy thought, "I'll take a ride on those funny stairs myself."

She got on the moving stairs and rode up to the next floor.

When she got off, she saw some more moving stairs. So she rode up to the next floor.

On each floor Nancy saw more moving stairs. She rode up, up, up. She had so much fun that she forgot all about looking for Susan.

At last Nancy reached the top floor.
"Oh!" she thought. "I must go right
back to the place where the toys are.
Mrs. Hall said we should meet her near
the clock in half an hour."

Nancy got into an elevator and went
down to another floor. But the only things
she found were kitchen chairs and tables
and hundreds of pots and pans.

Nancy was puzzled and wondered what
to do. She went to another floor. No
toys there, either. No roller skates or
dolls or airplanes. Nothing but coats and
dresses. Dozens and dozens of them.

Now Nancy was more puzzled than ever. She hardly knew what to do, but at last she got into an elevator. Down she rode and got off at the next floor.

No toys there, either! And no Susan, no John, no Mrs. Hall.

How puzzled Nancy was! She didn't know how to find her friends. So she just walked around, looking for them.

At last she saw a window with a big sign that said, "Lost and Found."

"Oh," thought Nancy, "my friends are lost, and I want to have them found. I'll ask this lady in the window if she can find them for me."

Nancy said to the lady, "My friends are lost. I haven't seen them for an hour. I don't know what became of them. Can you find them for me?"

"Perhaps I can," said the lady. "Is your name Nancy Fox?"

"Yes, it is," said Nancy. She was surprised that the lady knew her name.

The lady picked up a telephone and said a few words to someone. Then she hung up the telephone.

"Stay right here," she said, smiling.

In a few minutes Mrs. Hall and Susan and John came rushing toward Nancy.

"Oh, Nancy," cried Susan, "we waited half an hour near the clock. Then we looked for you all over the whole store. It was awful to have you lost."

Nancy looked puzzled. "Why, Susan!" she said. "I wasn't lost. You were lost, but I'm glad I found you."

Ups and Downs

"Scamp! Scamp!" Mrs. Brown called to her pet monkey. "Come here!"

The little monkey was running away. He was running down a long hall in the Park Street Building.

Mrs. Brown and Jack, the elevator boy, were trying to catch him.

"Scamp!" Mrs. Brown called. "Come here!" And she stamped her foot.

But Scamp kept on running down the hall. Mrs. Brown couldn't catch him, and Jack couldn't catch him, either.

They were up on the fifth floor, and
Nancy was there, too. She was standing
in the hall beside the elevator.

As Scamp came near her, she reached
out to catch him. But the sly little
monkey jumped into the elevator.

"Pooh!" said Nancy. "It's not hard
to catch you." And she shut the door.

Jack rushed over to get the monkey.
But the elevator door wouldn't open.

"The elevator is going down!" Jack
called in surprise. "There isn't anybody
in it but Scamp. That smart little
monkey must be making it go."

Inside the elevator the little monkey saw the buttons that made it go.

Scamp pushed the button with 2 on it, and down went the elevator to the second floor. He pushed the button with 4 on it, and up went the elevator.

Scamp pushed one button after another. Swish, swish! Up and down went the elevator, and up and down went the little monkey, also. Up and down he rode, more than a dozen times. Nobody could stop him.

What fun Scamp had, playing with all those buttons!

Jack and Mrs. Brown stayed on the fifth floor near the elevator door. And Nancy stayed there, also.

Some other people came into the hall. They all wanted to ride down in the elevator.

A lady in a purple dress said to Jack, "Where's the elevator? I want to go down."

"I'm sorry," Jack answered, "but I can't take you down now. And I can't take anybody else down, either. There's a monkey in the elevator."

How everybody laughed!

"But I'm in a hurry," said the lady in the purple dress.

"I don't think you will have to wait long," Jack told her. "Soon the monkey will push the button that says 5. Then the elevator will stop here at the fifth floor, and the door will open."

But for a long time the monkey didn't happen to push the button that said 5. He pushed all the other buttons, and the elevator went on rushing up and down.

"Oh!" cried Nancy. "I'm the one who shut Scamp in the elevator. I'd like to do something to get him out."

But there wasn't a thing that Nancy could do! There wasn't a thing that anybody else could do, either!

At last Scamp happened to push the right button, the elevator stopped at the fifth floor, and the door opened.

Jack held the door open before the smart little monkey could push another button and start the elevator again.

"Quick, Nancy," he called. "Here's Scamp. Now there's something that you can do."

And this time there was something that Nancy could do.

Before the monkey could get away, Nancy picked him up and handed him to Mrs. Brown.

Scamp's ride was over!

"Well, Scamp!" Nancy said. "You were a funny elevator boy. You wouldn't take anybody up, and you wouldn't take anybody down, either. You rode all alone. That's no way to run an elevator."

"You are right," said Jack. "I'll run the elevator now. Going down! Going down! I'll take everybody down."

A Funny Balloon Ride

"Balloons! Balloons! Balloons!" called Mrs. Jolly. She was holding a bunch of balloons of many colors—yellow and red and green and blue and purple. They looked pretty, bobbing in the wind.

Every Saturday she came to the park to sell balloons to the children.

One morning John and Tommy and their friend Dick Pound came along and met Mrs. Jolly. Dick was carrying a big basket and also a clothesline.

Dick said, "Mrs. Jolly, I'd like to use your whole bunch of balloons. But I haven't enough money to buy them. I'd like to rent them for an hour."

"Rent them!" cried Mrs. Jolly, looking at the bobbing balloons. "Who ever heard of renting balloons? What would you do if you did rent them?"

Dick said, "I'd tie them to my basket. Then I'd fly up in the air in the basket. After a while I'd come down and give your balloons back. Then I'd pay you."

"Well, well!" laughed Mrs. Jolly. "How much rent would you pay?"

Dick pulled some money out of his pocket. "I have a dime and a nickel and five pennies," he said.

"Oh," said friendly Mrs. Jolly, "these balloons are not for rent. But I'll let you use them without paying rent."

"Thank you very much," said Dick.

Dick tied the bobbing balloons to the basket.

Mrs. Jolly held it down so that it couldn't go up in the air. John also helped Dick get ready. He tied one end of the clothesline to the basket.

"Now we're all ready," said Dick. "Hold the end of the clothesline," he told John and Tommy as he got in.

"When I'm ready to come down, I'll call to you. Then you must pull me down with the clothesline."

"Now, Mrs. Jolly, please let go of the basket," said Dick.

She let go, and the balloons bobbed up and down and pulled at the basket. But they couldn't pull it off the ground.

Dick was very much puzzled.

At last he said, "Perhaps I'm too heavy. You aren't so heavy, Tommy. You sit in the basket, and we'll see if the balloons can pull you up."

"All right," said Tommy, as he got in. "My toy bear and I aren't heavy."

But the balloons couldn't pull Tommy up, either. So he got out, while Dick held the basket. But Tommy forgot to take his toy bear out of the basket.

Just then Mrs. Jolly and the boys heard an airplane, and they looked up. They forgot all about the balloons.

Dick forgot to hold on to the basket, and John dropped the end of the long clothesline he was holding.

All at once Tommy shouted, "Look! Dick's basket is going up in the air! My bear is going up, too."

"Oh, my balloons!" cried Mrs. Jolly. "They will be lost. How awful!"

She tried to reach the clothesline, but it was too high for her. Away sailed the balloons, carrying the basket with them.

All at once a puff of wind blew the balloons toward a tree. The clothesline caught on one of the branches.

In a minute Dick climbed the tree and got the balloons. Then he climbed down and handed them to Mrs. Jolly.

"They aren't hurt at all," he said.

"Thank you for letting me use the balloons without paying any rent. I thought they would lift the basket up, and they did. They even took the little bear up, because he wasn't heavy. But they couldn't lift me up."

"No," said Mrs. Jolly, smiling. "Not this bunch of balloons. It would take a much bigger bunch to lift you up."

"Yes, I've learned that now," said Dick. "It would take more balloons than I can ever buy or rent. It would take hundreds and hundreds and hundreds of balloons to lift a big boy like me."

The Halloween Party

Two girls were coming down from the fifth floor of the Park Street Building.

"Jack, can you guess who we are?" one of them said to the elevator boy.

"Yes, I can guess," laughed Jack. "You are Nancy and Susan. Why do you have on those fancy clothes?"

Susan answered, "We're invited to a Halloween party at Sam Penny's, and we're on our way now. Sam invited the boys and girls in our room at school. They will all have on fancy clothes."

Soon Nancy and Susan were walking along the street.

"We're almost there," said Susan. "Look for a big brick house. That's where Sam lives."

Suddenly Nancy cried, "See that boy wearing a clown suit. I'm sure he's Joe. Yesterday Joe told me that he was going to rent a clown suit with big red spots on it."

Just then the clown went up the steps of a big brick house and knocked on the door. The girls followed him.

A lady who wore a pink dress met them at the door and said, "Come in."

The children at the Halloween party
all had on fancy clothes. One girl was
dressed like a fairy, with purple wings.
A boy was wearing a fireman's suit and
carrying a toy ladder.

One big boy wore a cowboy suit and
had a handkerchief around his neck.

A boy with feathers on his head was
dancing up and down with loud shouts.

Next to him was a funny scarecrow
with a big mouth. And an old woman as
ugly as a troll wore a purple coat and
a tall, pointed hat.

A large black cat with a long tail was
waving a paper pumpkin on a stick.

"Mew, mew!" he said. "I'm a kitty."

"Isn't he silly?" laughed Nancy.

Just then she saw a boy dressed like
a little pink pig, and another one dressed
like the big bad wolf. The pig held the
door open just a crack.

He looked at the wolf through the
crack and said, "By the hair of my
chinny-chin-chin, you are the wolf, and
you can't come in."

"Pooh," said the wolf. "I can, too."

The children sang and danced around
and played games for about an hour.

Then the lady said, "Now you may each
walk across the room. If your name is
guessed, you must uncover your face."

When the pumpkin girls walked across
the room, nobody guessed who they were.

Next came a boy in a dark blue coat
with silver buttons and a silver star.
He was wearing a policeman's cap.

"Ha!" shouted one of the boys. "Look
at that fat policeman! He's Sandy."

When the fat policeman uncovered his
face, Nancy was puzzled. "Why, he's a
stranger!" she whispered to Susan.

The next one that the children guessed was a white cat with a fiddle.

One by one the children in their fancy clothes walked across the room. As their names were guessed, they uncovered their faces.

"This is queer," Susan said to Nancy. "I thought Sam invited just the boys and girls in our room at school. But I must have been wrong. These children are all strangers."

"Anyway," said Nancy, "that's Joe wearing the clown suit."

But when the clown uncovered his face, Susan said, "Oh, he's not Joe. He's a stranger, too. We followed the wrong clown and came to the wrong house. That's why these children are strangers."

The lady who wore the pink dress smiled at Nancy and Susan. "We haven't guessed the pumpkin girls yet," she said.

Slowly the two girls uncovered their faces. They were almost ready to cry. Nancy even got out her handkerchief.

"I'm afraid we're at the wrong party," Susan said to the lady. "We were invited to Sam Penny's Halloween party."

"This is Johnny Ball's party," said the lady. "But we're all glad you came. You surprised us, and it's fun to have a surprise at a Halloween party."

She telephoned to Sam and told him where the girls were. Then she gave them sandwiches to eat and milk to drink. After they had ice cream and big pieces of cake, she took them to Sam's house.

And that is how Susan and Nancy went to two Halloween parties in one day.

Along
Country Roads

Bread and Jam

A Surprise at School

It was the very first day of school in the fall, and children from the farms nearby were coming down the roads toward the Maple Grove School.

Some of them rode in automobiles, and some walked. But Sarah Best was riding on Poky, her pet donkey.

The five Burns children didn't live far away, and so they were walking to school.

Betty Jane Burns hurried ahead of her brothers and sisters. When she saw Tom and Sarah Best, she waved to them. They waved back, and Sarah tried to make Poky hurry.

"Hee-haw, hee-haw," said the donkey.

"Be quiet, Poky," said Sarah. "And hurry up. Miss Valentine is waiting for us."

She waved to the teacher, who was standing at the door of the little brick schoolhouse.

Soon all the boys and girls were at the Maple Grove School.

Ding-dong, ding-dong went the bell. All the children hurried inside and sat down at their desks to work.

Some of them read their new books, and some began to write letters telling what they had done in the summer.

Tom Best got out some drawing paper and began to draw. Soon he had made a picture of a woodpecker.

All of a sudden there was a buzzing sound. Z-z-z, zzz, zzz! Two wasps were flying around Betty Jane's desk.

"Oh! Wasps! Wasps!" she screamed, as she dropped her pen. "They will sting me."

Tom jumped up from his desk and knocked the wasps down with a piece of drawing paper. Then he took them to the window and dropped them outside.

Suddenly there was a loud hee-haw at a window, and Poky stuck his head in. He waved his ears and rolled his eyes.

"Hee-haw, hee-haw, hee-haw!" said the donkey, and then he galloped away.

Sarah jumped up from her desk and hurried to the window.

"There are more wasps outside," she said. "And Poky is galloping toward the woods. He's afraid the wasps will sting him."

"I'll catch him," said Don Burns, getting up from his desk. He ran outdoors, but he came right back.

"The air is full of wasps!" he said.

Miss Valentine shut the windows, so that no more wasps could get inside.

"Now," said the teacher, "we'll have to think of a way to get rid of the wasps, or we can't go outdoors."

After a minute Betty Jane said, "I've thought of a way to get rid of them. We have hives of honey bees at home, and I know that bees like sweet things. Don't wasps like sweet things, too?"

"Yes," answered Miss Valentine, "they do like sweet things."

"We have something sweet in our lunch boxes," said Betty Jane. "We have jam sandwiches. Don could take some of the sandwiches outside and walk away from the schoolhouse. Wouldn't the wasps follow the jam?"

"Maybe they would," said the teacher. "That seems like a wise plan."

"Oh!" cried Sally Ann Burns. "I'd hate to have the wasps sting Don."

"We won't let them sting him," said the teacher. "We'll cover him up."

She opened a door and took out her raincoat and an old straw hat with a pink ribbon on it. Don laughed as he put on the long coat and the hat with the ribbon. He buttoned the coat and pulled the hat down on his head.

"Won't the wasps sting Don's face and hands?" asked Sally Ann.

"We'll cover them, also," answered Miss Valentine. "Then Don will be safe."

When Don's face and hands were covered, he was a funny sight.

"The wasps can't scare me now," said Don. "Where are the jam sandwiches?"

Betty Jane got a sandwich and put a piece of bread and jam on each of Don's hands.

"I'd like a bite myself," she said. "I hate to feed this jam to the wasps."

"Never mind," said Don. "We have more sandwiches."

He held his hands carefully, so that the pieces of bread wouldn't fall off.

Don was so much shorter than Miss Valentine that the coat came almost to the ground. It flapped around his legs and got in his way. He had to lift each foot carefully as he walked.

"I'd hate to wear these clothes all the time," he laughed. "I'm walking slower than I've ever walked before."

Tom Best opened the door, and Don stepped out of the schoolhouse.

The children left their desks and ran
to the windows to watch Don.

Sure enough, the wasps were following
him. A few had lighted on the jam.

Slowly and carefully Don walked down
the path toward the woods. The long
coat flapped against his legs. It flapped
against them with every step he took.

More and more wasps followed him,
until each piece of bread and jam was
covered all over with wasps.

Betty Jane's plan was working. All
the wasps were following the sweet jam.

The children saw Don go into the woods. Soon he came out, riding on Poky.

"Don doesn't have the pieces of bread and jam any more," cried Betty Jane. "He left them in the woods. My plan worked! He got rid of the wasps."

Don had uncovered his face, but he still wore the hat with the pink ribbon. The long coat flapped against the little donkey's sides at every step. How the children laughed at the funny sight!

Don hitched Poky to a tree and ran inside.

"Hurrah! Hurrah!" he shouted. "We have got rid of the wasps. And they didn't sting me. Betty Jane's plan worked."

"Yes," said Tom Best, "but I can see the wasps' nest in the tree outside the window. Maybe they'll come back to it."

"I'll take the nest down," said Don.

He covered his face and hands again. Then he went out, still wearing Miss Valentine's coat and the hat with the pink ribbon.

He put a ladder against the tree. Carefully he climbed up the ladder and took the nest down. Not a wasp flew out as Don carried the nest away.

"Well," said Sally Ann, "the wasps' nest is gone, and so are they. Don got rid of them with the bread and jam."

A Wish That Came True

The Circus Comes to the Farm

One afternoon, when the Burns children were walking home from school, they stopped to look at the circus sign by the road.

They passed the sign every day, but they never got tired of seeing it.

"Look at those elephants and lions and that fierce tiger!" cried Sally Ann. "See the funny clowns! Oh, how I wish we were going to the circus!"

"Yes," said David. "I hate to miss it."

The circus was coming to Spring City the next day. But the Burns children couldn't go to see it. They didn't have enough money to buy tickets.

"We can see the parade in Spring City tomorrow," said Don. "We don't need any tickets for the parade."

"And that will be a wonderful sight," said Betty Jane. "We'll see elephants and giraffes and fierce lions and tigers. And we'll hear the band play."

"Elephants and giraffes and a band," sang Sally Ann. "And fierce tigers and lions! They'll all be in the parade."

She ran uphill ahead of the others. Suddenly she shouted, "I see elephants!"

"Oh, pooh!" laughed Don. "You can't fool us. Wait until tomorrow. Then you will really see elephants in the parade. You'll see tigers and giraffes, too."

"I don't see any giraffes," called Sally Ann. "But I really do see elephants!"

The others hurried up the hill. They really did see two great big elephants, and they also saw circus trucks in front of their farm. What a wonderful sight! It was almost too good to be true.

There was a truck full of ponies, and there was also a fancy truck with a picture of a fierce lion. Above it was the word, "Lion."

Another fancy truck had a picture of a tiger, and the letters above it said, "Tiger."

The circus men were shouting and running around. And no wonder! There was something wrong! A big red and gold truck had gone off the road, and its wheels were stuck in the sand.

The men were getting ready to hitch the elephants to the red and gold truck.

The five children ran toward the truck. Just then their mother and father and little brother Bobby came from the house.

"Hurrah, hurrah!" shouted Bobby. "The circus has come to us! I see a lion and a tiger, but where's the band?"

"The band is with the other part of the circus," one of the men answered. "It has gone ahead to Spring City."

"Where are the clowns?" said Bobby. "I want to see the clowns."

"I am a clown," answered the man, "even if I don't have on my clown suit. My name is Buzz. I'm taking care of this part of the circus, and these men are my helpers."

Buzz turned to Mrs. Burns and said, "We have been on the road since early this morning, and we must get to Spring City tonight. But we can't go ahead until we pull this truck out of the sand."

Mrs. Burns invited the circus men to stay for supper.

As she walked toward the house, she thought, "I'll make sandwiches for the men. There's bread baking in the oven, and I have plenty of cold chicken, and some butter that I just churned. They'll have enough to eat."

The children watched the circus men. First some of the men hitched the big gray elephants to the truck. Then the elephants began to pull. Very, very slowly they drew the big red and gold truck out of the deep sand and back on the road.

The Clown's Magic Tricks

Mr. Burns helped the circus men bring cool water for the animals. Then all the men went to the house for supper. The children came running behind them.

After supper Buzz did some tricks. He kept five gold balls in the air at once. He stood on his head and walked on his hands. He skipped rope and fell down and rolled over and over.

At last Buzz said, "Bobby, do you suppose you'll know me at the circus? I'll be dressed in my clown suit, and my face will be painted."

"I won't see you," said Bobby. "We aren't going to the circus, because we don't have enough money for tickets."

"But we're going to see the parade," said Don. "We'll see Buzz marching in the parade behind the bandwagon."

"And right now I'll show you some magic tricks," said Buzz. "Watch me."

He went over to Mrs. Burns. "Dear me!" he said. "What do you suppose this is in your hair?"

He drew a dollar bill out of her hair. Then he drew out three more dollar bills.

"For our supper," he said, as he paid her the four dollars.

The children opened their eyes very wide. Could it be true? Dollar bills in their mother's hair!

Then Buzz said to Mr. Burns, "It's very queer for a man to hide money behind his ears." He drew some dollar bills from behind Mr. Burns's ears.

"For bringing water to the animals," he said, giving Mr. Burns the money.

75

"I never saw such a funny family!"
said Buzz, with a big smile.

He went over to Bobby's chair and
pulled a ticket from under his nose. A
ticket to the circus! Buzz went around to
all the family and found a ticket under
every nose. It seemed too good to be true!

As Buzz gave the tickets to Mr. Burns,
he said, "Here are your tickets. I'll see
you at the circus tomorrow."

"Thank you!" cried all the family.

And that's how their wish came true.

Benny's Trick

The next Friday afternoon after school David Burns was marching around the farmyard. As he marched, he blew on a little horn. Toot! Toot! Toot!

He blew and marched, and marched and blew. Right behind him marched Benny, the young rooster that was his pet.

Benny had been David's pet ever since he was a baby chicken. David thought that Benny was a wonderful pet.

Toot! Toot! Toot! Toot! David blew on his horn, and they both marched along.

Benny had just learned how to do this trick. For a week David had been trying to teach it to him.

At first the rooster hadn't followed him. But David had kept on trying to teach him the trick. And at last Benny had learned to do it very well.

David thought it was a good trick. His brothers and sisters also thought it was a good trick. It was a better trick than they could teach their pets.

The Burns children had seen the circus parade the week before, and now they wanted to have a pet parade. All the other children at the Maple Grove School wanted to have a parade, too.

So Miss Valentine had told them they could have a pet parade and invite all the people who lived near the school.

David was getting the rooster ready for the pet parade.

Saturday morning David waked up very early because he heard a loud noise outside. Chug, chug, chug! A truck was coming into the yard.

David was sleepy, but he got right up to see what was happening. In a few minutes he was dressed and outdoors.

He saw Mr. Huff, who often came to buy chickens and eggs from Mr. Burns. Mr. Huff was sliding a box of chickens into his truck.

David's eyes opened wide. What do you suppose he saw? Benny was in the box with the other chickens!

David ran straight to the truck as fast as he could. But before he could get there, Mr. Huff had climbed in and was ready to drive away.

"Oh, oh, Mr. Huff!" David screamed. "Don't take Benny! He's my pet! Don't! There's a mistake! There's a mistake!"

But the engine was going chug, chug. David's voice was loud, but the engine was louder. Mr. Huff didn't hear him.

There wasn't time for David to call his father. There was only one thing to do. He must go with Benny.

So he made a quick jump and climbed into the back of the truck.

Away they went to Spring City. It wasn't a very long trip, and soon Mr. Huff was stopping in his own yard.

David jumped down. How surprised Mr. Huff was to see him!

"Mr. Huff," cried David, "there's been an awful mistake. Benny is in your truck. He's my pet, and I've been teaching him to do a trick for the parade next Friday."

"Why, David!" said Mr. Huff. "Which one of these chickens is your pet?"

"That yellow one," answered David. "If you'll take him out, I'll show you that he's my pet."

Mr. Huff took the yellow rooster out of the box and put him on the ground. The little rooster flapped his wings and tried to crow.

David pulled the horn out of his pocket. He took a deep breath and began to blow. Toot! Toot! Then he walked away.

He wasn't sure that Benny would be able to remember his trick. But the little rooster marched along behind him, in time with the toots of the horn.

"That's a funny trick," said Mr. Huff, smiling. "I'm sure that chicken is yours."

Then Mr. Huff counted the chickens, and found one too many.

"Of course there's a mistake," he said. "I suppose your chicken got in with the others last night. Now I'll take you and your pet home."

"Hurrah!" cried David. "Benny and I can be in the parade next Friday."

Sarah's Plan

One Tuesday afternoon Sarah Best was looking at an old buggy that had not been used for years and years. It was covered with dust, and there was an old wren's nest under the seat.

There were big holes in the top and cracks in the floor. The wheels looked as if they could hardly stand up.

"Poky," said Sarah, "I know something you can do in our parade on Friday. You can pull that buggy, and I'll drive. You are so much smaller than the old buggy that you'll look funny pulling it."

"Hee-haw, hee-haw," said Poky.

Sarah hitched Poky to the fence. Then she ran to tell her mother and her brother Tom what she wanted to do.

"Do you suppose Poky will be able to pull that big buggy?" she asked.

"Of course he will," said her mother.

Tom hitched Poky to the buggy, and Sarah got up on the seat. She spoke to the donkey, and off he trotted, while the buggy squeaked along behind.

All at once Poky stood still. Sarah spoke to him, and Tom spoke to him, but he wouldn't take a step.

"Hee-haw, hee-haw, hee-haw!" he said.

"Oh, dear," said Sarah. "He never stopped like this before. What's the matter with you, Poky? Are you a lazy little donkey?"

"I don't think he's lazy," said Tom. "He just doesn't feel like going. He will start when he feels like it."

At last the little donkey started.

The next day and the next Sarah drove around the yard in the buggy, but Poky didn't stop again.

All the same, Sarah was afraid that he might stop in the parade on Friday, just the way he had stopped on Tuesday.

She kept trying to think of something to do if he should stop in the parade.

At last she thought of a plan. She tied a piece of string to a long stick, and tied a small bunch of hay to the other end of the string. Then Sarah put the whole thing under the seat of the buggy.

On Friday all the fathers and mothers
and grandfathers and grandmothers came
to the school.

Soon the parade began. David Burns
came first. He took a deep breath and
began blowing on his horn. Toot! Toot!
His pet rooster marched behind him.

David's sister, Betty Jane, was pushing
a doll buggy with two kittens in it.

Jill Nickel held tight to Easter Bunny,
her pet rabbit, and Jim had brought
Pinky, his pet pig. Billy had a squirrel
on his shoulder. How it chattered!

A puppy trotted along beside Dick with a wag, wag, wag of his short black tail.

Poky came next, with Sarah riding in the old buggy. She looked back over her shoulder and saw the rest of the parade. Don had his spotted calf, and Molly had Waddle, her pet goose.

Of course the crowd clapped for all the pets, but they clapped loudest for the donkey hitched to the old buggy.

Poky became frightened at the noise and stood still. Sarah spoke to him, but she wasn't able to make him go.

All the people clapped harder.

Sarah spoke louder to Poky. Then she shouted, but he stood still, just as he had on Tuesday. So she reached down under the seat and picked up something which lay on the floor. It was the long stick with the hay tied to it.

Very carefully she pushed it out until the bunch of hay hung just in front of Poky's nose. She held her breath and waited to see what Poky would do.

"He ought to go now," thought Sarah.

The donkey looked, and he sniffed. Then he reached out his head for the bunch of hay. He couldn't get the hay, and so he took a step. But when he moved ahead, of course the bunch of hay moved ahead, too.

So he took another step and another and another. Sarah's plan was working. The buggy was moving again.

The people clapped hard and laughed until they were out of breath.

When the parade was over, Miss Valentine said to Sarah, "Poky was the funniest animal in the parade! The very funniest! He ought to get a prize."

"Of course he ought to," said Sarah. "I'll feed him the hay for a prize."

She held the bunch of hay nearer to Poky, and in one big bite the donkey gobbled up his prize.

Pinky at the Fair

Jill laughed as Jim's little pig tried to wiggle away. She held on tight to the wet pig, while Jim scrubbed and rubbed. He scrubbed so hard that Jill could feel drops of water splashing like rain.

Jim was getting Pinky ready for the pet show at the Fair in Spring City.

At last the fat little pig was washed.

"There!" cried Jim. "Doesn't Pinky look beautiful and clean? She ought to win a prize at the Fair."

The next day the Nickel family went to the Fair, taking Easter Bunny and Pinky. Around the pig's neck Jim had fastened a bell, which rang and rang.

At the Fair they saw large crowds of people—farmers and city people.

The band was playing, and there was a merry-go-round with all kinds of animals. Round and round they galloped—lions, tigers, giraffes, roosters, and geese, with children riding on them.

Men were selling colored balloons for a dime and sticks of candy for a penny.

Soon Jim found the place for the pet show. It was a ring with a rope around it.

Jim marched along, looking over his shoulder at Pinky. The bell on her neck rang—ting-a-ling.

Behind Jim came a girl with a puppy and a boy with a rabbit. A big white hen looked over a boy's shoulder at a kitten in a basket. "Cluck, cluck," went the hen, and "Mew," went the kitten.

Don had his spotted calf. He held on tight to the rope that was fastened around its neck. "Ma-ma-aa!" said the calf.

Behind the calf came a boy carrying a crow in a cage. A girl held a duck tight in her arms, and behind her waddled two geese that belonged to Ellen.

Jim saw Jill on the other side of the ring with Easter Bunny. He also saw a sheep that belonged to a big boy. He saw a turtle, a goat hitched to a wagon, and even a ground hog.

What a lot of noise there was in that ring! There were mew-mews, cluck-clucks, and quack-quacks. There were grunts and squawks and squeaks and squeals.

A crowd of about a hundred people was outside the ring, watching the show.

Three men stood in the middle of the ring, to pick out the best-looking pet.

When all the pets had gone around the ring, one of the men fastened a blue ribbon on a beautiful big dog.

The man said, "Jay wins the prize for the best-looking pet. He gets the blue ribbon. Jay belongs to Bill White of the Hill Top School."

Jay wagged his tail, while everyone clapped.

"Now," said one of the men, "we'll see which pet can do the funniest trick. That pet will win a blue ribbon, too."

"Pinky can't do tricks," thought Jim. "She won't get a prize."

He looked for the way out of the ring, but he couldn't find it. ˌAround he went, with the pig close behind him like a shadow. Ting-a-ling rang her bell.

When Jim slowed down, Pinky slowed down, too. Ting—a—ling.

People began to laugh.

Jim thought, "They are laughing at me because I can't get out of the ring."

Poor Jim! His face got as red as fire. A hundred people laughing at him!

He ran faster, and the pig raced after him. They ran around that ring nine times, but Jim just couldn't find the way out.

The people laughed harder and harder. A hundred people laughing at Jim!

He ran until he was out of breath. Where, oh, where was the way out? At last he saw it right in front of him.

As the boy and the pig left the ring, all the people laughed harder than ever.

Jim wanted to see who would win the blue ribbon for the funniest trick. So he watched the pets do their tricks.

A cat played with a ball, and a white kitten jumped from a boy's shoulder and into a basket.

One dog jumped over a wagon, and another went tap, tap on a toy drum. A crow pulled a letter out of a boy's pocket and cried, "Caw! Caw! Caw!"

At last one of the men called to Jim, "Bring your trick pig over here."

Slowly Jim went back into the ring, and Pinky followed right behind him.

"She can't do any tricks," said Jim.

"Oh, we think she can," said the man. "She follows close behind you like a shadow. She runs or walks or stops just when you do. We think that's the funniest trick a pig could do."

Then he said, "Pinky wins the blue ribbon for the funniest trick. She belongs to Jim Nickel of Maple Grove School."

The people clapped and clapped. A hundred people clapping for Jim!

How Tom Went to the Fair

It was the second day of the Fair, the day of the airplane races. How Tom and Sarah wanted to see those races!

The races weren't going to begin until noon, but the children wanted to be at the Fair by ten o'clock. After breakfast the family hurried to do their work, so that they would be able to start at half past nine.

But as they drove by their pasture, Father cried, "Here's some bad luck. The cows are out of the pasture. I'll have to stop and drive them back into the pasture and fix the fence."

"Oh, Father!" cried Sarah. "Can't we go to the Fair and see the races?"

Before his father could answer, Tom said, "I'll drive the cows out and fix the fence. I know how to fix it, because I helped build it."

"But the races begin at noon!" cried Sarah. "You'll miss them."

"No, I won't," said Tom. "When I finish, I'll walk to Uncle Zeke's and get a ride. It's only half a mile."

"All right," said Father. "Uncle Zeke and Aunt Kitty will start at eleven o'clock. You'll get to town before the races begin. Here's a ticket to the Fair."

Tom got out of the car and watched the family ride off. Then he went after a hammer and some boards and nails.

Before he could begin to fix the fence, he had to drive the cows back into the pasture. That wasn't easy.

"Moo! Moo!" went the cows. "Moo! Moo! Moo!" They wanted to stay right there and eat, but at last Tom finished driving them into the pasture.

He knew it was late, because the shadows were getting shorter. And he couldn't quit now, for he still had to fix the fence. He had to nail the boards carefully in place.

By the time he had finished nailing the boards, the sun was high in the sky. The shadows were still shorter.

"It must be eleven o'clock already," he thought. "By this time Aunt Kitty and Uncle Zeke have gone to the Fair."

Poor Tom. How he hated to miss the races! He picked up the hammer and the nails that were left and started slowly toward the house. No use hurrying now. It was already too late to go with Uncle Zeke and Aunt Kitty.

All at once Tom heard an airplane up in the sky. It flew in a great circle above him. Then it circled lower and lower and landed in the pasture.

Tom could hardly believe his eyes. An airplane landing in the pasture! He went racing toward it.

A stranger got out of the airplane.

"Hello," he said. "I've been flying around in a circle, trying to find Spring City. How many miles is it from here?"

"Twenty-nine miles north," said Tom.

"I'm glad it's only twenty-nine miles," said the stranger. "It's already half past eleven, and I'm supposed to be in the airplane races at noon."

"Oh!" cried Tom. "The airplane races! Sarah and Mother and Father will see you. They started for the Fair between nine and ten o'clock."

"Why didn't you go yourself?" asked the stranger.

"We had some bad luck," Tom said. Then he told the man about the fence.

"I have a ticket for the Fair," said Tom. "I was going to walk half a mile north and get a ride with Uncle Zeke. But I didn't finish my work until after eleven. He must have started already."

"Well," said the man, "I think we can turn your bad luck into good luck. Hop into the airplane. I'll take you to the Fair myself. We ought to be there in a few minutes if it's only twenty-nine miles north of here."

Tom was so excited that he couldn't say a word. He just got in.

When the engine started, it sounded as loud as a threshing machine. In a minute the airplane rolled across the pasture and sailed up off the ground.

Up it sailed, toward the sky. Below
them the roads looked like ribbons
between the green fields. The houses
and barns down below looked like toys,
and so did the horses and cows.

The airplane flew north and was soon
circling above the Fair Grounds. Below
him, Tom saw crowds of people hurrying
about like busy little bugs.

The airplane was circling lower and
lower, and the people down below were
beginning to look larger.

Tom saw hundreds of people looking up to watch the airplane land. Most of them were strangers, but he could see some of his school friends in the crowd.

When the airplane landed, his mother and father and Sarah came running up. Uncle Zeke and Aunt Kitty were close behind them.

How surprised they were to see Tom step out of the airplane! They were very proud of him, and of course he was proud, too. For he was the only boy who had ever come to the Fair in an airplane.

Peter, Peter, Pumpkin Grower

The Pumpkin That Went to the Fair

Early one morning Mr. Strong and his son Peter were in the cornfield, looking at the pumpkins that grew there.

The pumpkins belonged to Peter. He had raised them all by himself. When he looked at them, he remembered how hard he had worked all summer. Digging in the soft earth, raking, planting seeds, pulling weeds, and hoeing.

It had been fun to watch the plants come up. At first each one had been just two wee green leaves. But as the weather got hotter, the plants grew until they were big vines with pumpkins on them.

"Just look at the pumpkins I raised from a few seeds!" Peter said to his father. "Every vine is full of pumpkins."

"Yes," Mr. Strong said to his son. "There are hundreds of pumpkins. I really think you raised too many."

"Oh, Father!" cried Peter. "I couldn't raise too many pumpkins. Mother can bake lots of pumpkin pies. I think she has one in the oven right now. M-m-m."

"But we can't use all these pumpkins for pies," laughed Peter's father.

Peter said, "I know something else to do with one of them. I told our teacher that I'd take one of mine to the Fair."

For twenty minutes Peter and his father looked between the rows of corn, until they found the very biggest pumpkin.

"I'll take it to the Fair for you this morning," said Mr. Strong.

The next day the children from Peter's school went to the Fair in a big bus.

They went straight to the Children's Building. A children's band was playing there. Paintings and drawings made by children hung in rows on one wall. Dolls' dresses hung on another wall.

Miss Valentine and the children walked between long rows of tables, and saw big bunches of roses and other flowers. They saw some canned fruit and dozens of glasses of jam.

A girl named May pointed to a glass of jam with a blue ribbon on it.

"That glass of jam is mine," she said. "I raised the fruit in my garden."

There were also apples and other fruit, corn, cabbages, wheat, and potatoes.

One potato had a blue ribbon. "That's mine. It grew in my garden," said a boy. "I had twenty rows of potatoes."

Peter ran to a table near the wall. "See this big pumpkin with the card and the blue ribbon," he said. "It's mine!"

And it was his. The card on it said, "Peter, Peter, Pumpkin Grower."

There were nine other pumpkins. Not one of those nine pumpkins was the size of Peter's. Not one was half the size!

"Oh!" shouted Don. "Peter got the blue ribbon because he raised the biggest pumpkin. Hurrah for Peter!"

The Pumpkins Turn into a Bicycle

The next day Peter said, "Father, may I sell pumpkins at the stand where you sold fruit last summer? I could earn enough money for a bicycle."

Mr. Strong smiled at his son. "All right," he said. "But you'll have to sell a lot of pumpkins to buy a bicycle."

Peter painted a new sign with big red letters and nailed it to the stand. He put his bank in the stand, too.

Mr. Strong brought the pumpkins from the field. Pumpkins of different sizes, large, middle-sized, and small.

PETER, PETER, PUMPKIN GROWER

Soon a car stopped, and a pleasant woman bought a small-sized pumpkin.

"I want to bake some pies for my family," she said. She paid Peter a dime, and he put the dime in his bank.

Every day Peter would sell a dozen or more pumpkins of different sizes. And every day he would write down how many he had sold and also how much money he had earned for his bicycle.

One day a stranger drove up in an empty truck.

"How much will you take for a truck load of pumpkins?" he asked.

Peter didn't know what to say. He had never sold so many. But just then Mr. Strong came along. He told his son that he could sell a load of pumpkins for ten dollars.

"Sold!" said the stranger. "I'll pay ten dollars for a load of pumpkins."

Peter and his father helped the man load the truck. Soon it was filled.

The man paid Peter ten dollars and drove off with his load.

The stand was empty now. All the pumpkins were sold, and Peter counted his money. Besides the ten-dollar bill, he had eight dollars in change in his bank.

"Father," he cried, "I have enough money for a bicycle. I have nearly twenty dollars."

"Fine!" said his father. "Then your pumpkins will turn into a bicycle."

The Traveling Christmas Tree

Sarah's Secret

At Maple Grove School the children were getting ready for their Christmas party. They had invited all the neighbors.

They trimmed their tree with glass balls of different sizes and ropes of silver. They hung stars on it and put the biggest star on top.

What a beautiful sight the tree was— all gold and silver and red and green!

Jim and Jill were the only children who weren't at school.

"Their mother telephoned to me this morning," said Miss Valentine. "She told me that they will have to stay at home for about two weeks, and they can't have anybody visit them."

"Then they won't be able to come to the party on Friday," cried Sarah. "And they won't get their gifts or see the Christmas tree."

For a few seconds every child was so quiet you could have heard a pin drop.

Then Sarah ran to her desk and began to write something on a card. She gave the card to Miss Valentine.

When the teacher had read it, she said, "Sarah has thought of a very good plan. But she wants to keep it a secret until tomorrow."

"A secret!" cried Peter. "What fun!"

Santa Claus Comes

On Friday afternoon one automobile after another drove up to the school. The neighbors from the different farms were all coming to the Christmas party.

When Mr. Best and his wife drove up, Tom and Sarah weren't with them. The back seat of the car was empty.

But after about twenty minutes Tom and Sarah came riding up in a big sled. It was fine winter weather, and Poky trotted along over the snow.

"Whoa, Poky! Whoa, there!" called Tom, and the sled came to a stop.

Everyone went inside and sat down. The walls were trimmed with green branches tied with red ribbons. The green branches were fastened on the walls between the windows. And there was holly on the door.

On the teacher's desk stood the Christmas tree—all gold and silver and red and green.

The writing on the blackboard behind her desk said, "Merry Christmas to all."

First they sang some songs, and then Miss Valentine read a story.

Against the back wall there was a big chimney made of paper that looked like bricks. Out of the chimney came a fat, jolly man, who wore a red suit and cap.

The children laughed and clapped.

"Hello, Santa Claus!" they cried, but they thought he looked like Mr. Burns.

Santa Claus had a big sack of gifts— one for every child. He drew out a story book, a puzzle, a paint box, a toy sailboat, a little threshing machine, and two wee green buses.

Still the sack wasn't empty. Santa Claus drew out a tiny horse and wagon, a handkerchief done up in fancy holly paper, five balls of different sizes, and a duck that could go quack, quack.

When every child had a gift, the mothers passed around chocolate ice cream with Christmas cookies, and also fruit, chocolate candy, and nuts.

When they had finished eating, the teacher asked Sarah to tell her secret.

Sarah went up to the teacher's desk and said, "I thought it would be fun to take the Christmas tree to Jim and Jill. Poky can draw it on the sled."

"So that is your secret!" said Santa Claus. "A traveling Christmas tree for Jim and Jill!"

He lifted the tree from the desk and carried it to the sled. Tom helped him nail the Christmas tree stand to the sled, so that the tree couldn't fall over.

Under the tree the children put a sack of chocolate candy and a sack of fruit and nuts. In the sled Santa Claus put a doll and a book for Jill and a ball and a jumping jack for Jim.

Then Santa Claus said, "Go ahead, Sarah. We will come in the cars."

Sarah spoke to Poky and drove off.

The Tree Travels

Tom led the donkey over the snow. And Don walked along beside the tree to see that it didn't fall over.

One child had trimmed Poky's head with ribbon, and another child had put pieces of holly between his ears.

Tom had fastened some little silver bells underneath Poky's ears. As he led the donkey along, the bells rang out. Ting-a-ling! Ting-a-ling! Ting-a-ling!

After a while Sarah drove up to the house where Jim and Jill lived.

Tom led Poky right up to the porch. "Whoa, Poky!" he said. "Whoa!"

Then the automobiles came driving up, and Santa Claus and the other people stepped out.

Mrs. Nickel saw them through the window and ran to get Jim and Jill.

Very soon the two children were at the window. How excited they looked!

Who wouldn't be excited to see a Christmas tree come riding up to the door! A traveling Christmas tree—all gold and silver and red and green!

Who wouldn't be excited to see a gay Christmas party in the yard! And Santa Claus coming right up to the porch!

In his jolly voice Santa Claus called out, "Let's sing a song for Jim and Jill."

Santa led the song in his big, deep voice, and everybody sang with him,

"Jingle bells, jingle bells,
Jingle all the way."

Just then Poky shook his head, and the bells underneath his ears rang. Jingle, jingle, jingle they went.

Everybody laughed and Sarah said, "Hear Poky's bells go jingle, jingle! He is helping us with our song."

Then Tom went to the window and held up the jumping jack for Jim to see. Sarah held up the doll for Jill.

Santa Claus lifted the tree from the sled and put it on the porch. Don put some things in a circle underneath the tree—the ball and the book, some fruit and nuts, some chocolate candy, and a bunch of holly tied with red ribbon.

Mr. Nickel came out on the porch and thanked all the people. Then he took the tree and the gifts into the house.

Jim and Jill were very happy. They couldn't go to the tree, but a traveling Christmas tree had come to them.

On the Road

to Story-Land

A Ride to Animal Town

One day Billy Beaver was riding to Animal Town. Johnny Fox was hitched to his wooden cart. The day was warm, and Johnny Fox walked along slowly.

After a while Billy Beaver saw a tired old bunny by the side of the road.

"Whoa!" Billy called. "Whoa, there!"

Then he said to the bunny, "If you are going to Animal Town, hop in!"

The tired old bunny picked up his red jacket and hopped in, but he didn't say a word.

After a little while the rabbit said something very soft and low.

"What did you say?" asked Billy.

"Oh, nothing."

"Yes, you did. You said something."

"Oh, I just said that your wooden cart is hard to sit on."

"Then put your jacket under you."

The tired old rabbit sat on his jacket.

They went on a little farther. Then the rabbit said something again. He said it very soft and low.

"What did you say?" Billy asked.

"Oh, nothing. Nothing at all."

"Yes, you did. I heard you."

"Oh, I just said that Johnny Fox goes very slowly."

"Johnny Fox is doing the best he can," said Billy Beaver. "The sun is hot, and he has gone three miles already."

"Oh," said the rabbit.

They went on farther, past a yellow house and a big garden.

By and by the tired old bunny began to grumble again. He said something very soft and low.

"What did you say?" asked Billy.

"Oh, nothing."

"Yes, you did," said Billy Beaver. "I heard you grumbling."

"I just said that I can't see what is in front of us. You're so wide."

"I can't help being wide," said Billy Beaver. "Beavers are always wide."

They went on farther, and after a while they came to a wooden bridge. Bumpety-bumpety-bump went the wheels of the cart, and the tired old bunny grumbled again.

"What did you say this time?" asked Billy Beaver.

"Oh, nothing."

"Yes, you did. I heard you grumbling."

"Well, I just said that this bridge underneath us is so bumpy that it shakes me all around and hurts my tail."

Then Billy Beaver called, "Whoa, there! Whoa!" And he looked around at the old rabbit.

"Better get out, Rabbit," he said.

"Get out!" said the rabbit. "Why?"

"If you don't like to ride, you had better get out and walk."

"But I do like to ride," said the rabbit, staying right where he was.

"You don't behave as if you liked it," said Billy Beaver. "You keep grumbling and saying things very soft and low.

"You said that this wooden cart is hard to sit on. You said that Johnny Fox goes slowly. You said that you couldn't see what is in front of you.

"And now you say that this bridge underneath us is bumpy and shakes you. Better get out, Rabbit. Better get out and walk."

The rabbit looked at Billy Beaver. Then he hopped down and began to walk along the hot road, with his jacket over his shoulder.

The cart went along farther—past a big red barn and over a bridge.

As the rabbit walked along behind the cart, he got hotter and hotter. He took his handkerchief out of his jacket pocket and rubbed his face. At last he said something very soft and low.

"What did you say?" asked Billy.

"I said—let me get in and try again."

"Whoa," said Billy Beaver. "Whoa."

He thought a little while, and then he said, "All right. Get in."

The tired old bunny got in, but he didn't say a word.

After a long time the old rabbit said something very soft and low.

"Now you're grumbling again," said Billy Beaver. "What did you say?"

"I said—hot sun, bumpy road, tired old bunny feet. Glad to ride."

"Oh," said Billy Beaver. "Is that what you said? Now say one thing more."

"What?"

"Think it over, Rabbit."

They went along farther and farther on the bumpy road. Bumpety-bump.

At last the tired old bunny said something. "Glad to ride," he said. "THANK YOU!"

"That is polite," said Billy Beaver. "You are welcome, Rabbit! YOU'RE VERY WELCOME!"

Then Billy Beaver and the tired old bunny rode on to Animal Town.

Tippy Elephant's Hat

Tippy's Naughty Tricks

Tippy Elephant was a big gray baby who lived in a circus with her mother.

"Why do they call me Tippy?" asked the baby elephant one day.

"Because you tip around so," said her mother. "You put your front feet down so hard that you tip up behind. Then you put your back feet down so hard that you tip up in front."

"I like tipping back and forth," said the frisky little elephant.

131

What Tippy liked best was to stamp hard with her right front foot.

One afternoon she saw a little boy's balloon and stamped on it. Smash!

"Oh, Tippy!" said Mrs. Elephant. "I wish you would stop being so naughty. I wish you would behave yourself."

"I don't want to behave myself," said Tippy. "It's more fun to be frisky with my right front foot."

Then she saw a pail of water. Splash went her frisky front foot in the pail of water. The little elephant just wouldn't behave herself.

The next minute naughty little Tippy reached out her trunk and snatched a straw hat from a man's head. Then she dropped the hat on the ground and stamped on it with her frisky foot.

"You're a naughty, naughty baby!" cried Mrs. Elephant, shaking her head.

Almost every day some man would give Tippy an apple or some peanuts, and she would bow like a polite little elephant.

But then she would snatch the man's hat with her trunk. Stamp, stamp! She would smash the hat with her frisky front foot. One day she smashed eleven different hats.

At last one of the circus men said, "We'll have to sell that naughty little elephant if she doesn't behave better."

"Did you hear that?" Mrs. Elephant said to her child. "You'll have to learn to behave better. You'll have to stop smashing straw hats, or you can't travel with this circus."

"But it's fun being frisky with my foot!" cried naughty little Tippy. And she snatched three more hats and threw them down and smashed them flat.

Tippy Learns a Lesson

One afternoon Tippy thought, "Boys and girls often come to see me. Why can't I go to visit some of them?"

So she went tipping across a field. There she saw a shiny tin can and smashed it with her frisky foot.

In a yard she saw a little girl and a little boy digging in a sand box under a big colored umbrella. They each had a shiny tin pail and a tin shovel.

Tippy walked right into the yard.

"Run, Molly, run!" shouted the boy. Both children threw their shiny tin pails down in the sand. They threw their tin shovels down, too, and ran to the porch.

Then what do you suppose Tippy did? She lifted her frisky foot and knocked down the umbrella. Then she smashed the shiny tin pails. Bang! Bang! She smashed them both flat.

"Please stop!" cried the little boy. "If you'll stop spoiling our toys, I'll give you some peanuts."

He ran inside the house and got a big sack of peanuts. Tippy stepped up to the porch and took a peanut from the boy's hand with her trunk. When she had eaten it, she made a polite bow.

"Oh, you're thanking us," cried Molly. "You're welcome, baby elephant! You're very welcome!"

As Tippy took each peanut, she made a polite bow, and Molly said, "You're welcome." But when naughty Tippy had eaten all the peanuts, she smashed a tin shovel that lay near the porch.

"Please stop!" said Molly. "If you'll stop, I'll give you a lovely present."

Molly hurried into the house and got an old straw hat that was trimmed with a pink flower.

Tippy put her head down while Molly tied the hat on. Then Tippy made a polite bow and went tipping off to show her fancy new hat to her mother.

"Oh, Tippy, how sweet you look in that lovely hat!" cried Mrs. Elephant, when she saw her baby.

"Oh, Mr. Giraffe! Mr. Giraffe!" she called. "See Tippy's lovely new hat."

Tippy turned around slowly to show the giraffe how lovely the hat was.

The giraffe put his head down low to smell the pink flower. Two monkeys also came to look at the hat.

One of the circus men heard about Tippy's lovely hat and came to see it. Just then the baby elephant reached out her trunk and snatched the man's hat and threw it down on the ground.

And what do you suppose happened then?

Tippy's own hat fell off. Smash! Her frisky front foot landed on her own hat and smashed it flat.

"Oh, oh, oh!" cried the unhappy little elephant. "My hat with the lovely pink flower is spoiled! It's smashed flat."

The man, the giraffe, the monkeys, and Mrs. Elephant felt sorry for Tippy.

"It's too bad that your beautiful hat is spoiled," said the giraffe.

Mrs. Elephant said, "I'm sorry your hat is spoiled. You looked sweet in it. But you have learned a lesson. Now you know how unhappy the men feel when you spoil their hats."

"Yes, I've learned a lesson," said Tippy. "I'll never stamp on any more hats or balloons or tin pails. Never!"

And she never did.

Sojo

Sojo's Bright Idea

Sojo was a little boy who was always very, very sleepy.

One morning his mother called him early. "Get up, Sojo," she said. "Get up! After breakfast I want you to water the cabbages."

After Sojo had eaten his breakfast of porridge and milk, he walked slowly toward the pond to get some water.

When he was almost there, Sojo lay down under a tree to rest, and pretty soon he was fast asleep.

After a while Sojo woke up from his
nap, because he heard a splashing noise.
At the pond he saw a small elephant
splashing water with his trunk.

"It must be fun to do that," said Sojo,
opening his mouth in a big yawn.

"It isn't very much fun," said the little
elephant. "It's too easy."

Then Sojo remembered the cabbages
that needed watering, and suddenly he
had a bright idea.

"I know a place where splashing would
be fun," he said. "But it would be too
hard to splash there. You wouldn't be
able to do it. You are too small."

141

"Pooh!" cried the elephant. "I can splash anywhere. Show me the place."

The elephant begged and begged, until Sojo said, "Well, you're a friend of mine, and I don't want you to be unhappy. So I'll show you the place. Fill your trunk with water and follow me."

The baby elephant followed Sojo.

"This is a game," said Sojo. "You must sprinkle the water carefully on the cabbages. If you sprinkle all the rows just right, you get four points and win the game. You see, it's a hard game."

"Pooh," said the elephant, as he began to sprinkle the first row of cabbages. "This isn't hard. It's easy."

The elephant sprinkled water on all the cabbages in the garden, while Sojo sat and watched him.

At last the elephant said, "Now I've sprinkled water on all four rows. Does that count four points?"

"No," said Sojo. "You made a mistake and sprinkled too fast on one row."

"Please, won't you let me try again?" begged the little elephant.

"Well," said Sojo, "you're a friend of mine, and I hate to see you unhappy. You may try again tomorrow."

"Oh, thank you," said the elephant.

"You're welcome," Sojo answered with a yawn. "You're very welcome."

He lay down, and in a moment smart little Sojo was sound asleep.

When his mother woke him for lunch, she surely was surprised to see how well the cabbages had been watered.

Sojo's Second Bright Idea

After Sojo had eaten his lunch, his mother said, "Now I want you to cut the grass on the path."

Sojo went to look at the grass. He lay down underneath a tree, and soon he was fast asleep.

When he woke up from his nap, he saw a goat eating grass near the path.

Then Sojo had another bright idea.

"Hello!" he said with a yawn. "Don't you know you mustn't eat that grass?"

"Why not?" asked the goat.

"Because it doesn't belong to you. It belongs to us."

"Now, Sojo, be a good fellow," begged the goat. "Let me eat just a little."

"Well," said Sojo, "you are a friend of mine, and I hate to see you unhappy. I'll let you eat the grass on the path."

Then Sojo went back to sleep.

When Sojo woke, the goat had eaten
all the grass on the path. He begged
Sojo to let him eat some more grass.

"Not now," said Sojo. "Come back
next Tuesday, and I'll let you eat the
grass on the path again."

"Oh, thank you," said the goat.

"You're welcome," yawned Sojo, and
in a moment he was asleep again.

When Sojo's mother woke him from
his nap, she surely was surprised to see
how well the grass had been cut.

Sojo and Red Bird

After Sojo had finished his supper, he went to bed. He looked for Brown Bird, who came to the window every evening to sing until Sojo was asleep.

But this evening Brown Bird didn't come. Sojo thought he could not sleep until Brown Bird came to sing for him.

In a few moments a different bird with lovely red feathers came along and began to sing a soft, sweet song.

Again Sojo had a bright idea.

"Hello, Red Bird!" he called. "If you tried, maybe you could sing almost as well as Brown Bird."

"What is so wonderful about that fellow's song?" asked Red Bird.

"Well," answered Sojo, "Brown Bird can sing for an hour without stopping. Your song is sweet, but it's too short. You can't sing for a whole hour."

"Pooh!" said Red Bird, with a flap of his wings. "I can, too! I can sing longer than an hour."

He opened his mouth and sang and sang and sang.

"That's a good song," said Sojo, with a yawn. "Very—good—." And after a moment Sojo didn't say anything more.

When Red Bird had finished, he said, "Is my song as good as Brown Bird's?"

But he never did find out what Sojo thought, because Sojo was sound asleep.

Noisy Mr. Red Head

In the woods there was an old, old tree that stood on the bank of a river. That was where Mrs. Frisky and her babies had their home. They lived in a hole in a limb of the old tree.

Mrs. Frisky was a beautiful gray squirrel with a lovely big tail. And her six babies were just as beautiful. Mrs. Frisky loved those babies more than anything else in the world.

Too-oo was a wise old owl who had her home in the trunk of the same tree.

The owl was such a good neighbor that the squirrels all loved her.

Too-oo was kind and pleasant and polite. And she never made any noise or bothered anyone. In the daytime she was always asleep, and in the evening she flew off to hunt for food.

One day a stranger came to live in the tree. He was Mr. Red Head, the woodpecker. He was a noisy neighbor, always bothering Mrs. Frisky with his hammering.

Tick-tack, tick-tack-tack! The noisy fellow would drum on the limbs and the trunk of the tree, as he hunted for food.

One afternoon when he was drumming hard, the owl woke up and rushed out.

"That's a terrible noise!" she grumbled to Mrs. Frisky. "The wrens and the other birds don't bother us with awful noises. I hate to complain, but I wish we could get rid of Mr. Red Head."

"So do I," said Mrs. Frisky. "I love my babies too much to have them bothered by his noise."

"How in the world can I sleep?" the owl complained, with an angry flap of her wings. "I can't even get a nap. I'll hunt for a new home right now."

Away she flew.

Just then Mrs. Frisky saw two boys coming along the path by the river on their bicycles. From a high limb she watched them as they stopped under the tree. The boys made a fire of dry sticks and began to bake some potatoes.

Mrs. Frisky didn't like to see flames and smoke so close to the dry old tree. She watched until the boys had eaten their lunch and had stamped on the fire to put it out.

After they left, Mrs. Frisky felt safe. She and her babies went to sleep.

But Mr. Red Head was still watching. He saw a little smoke and some tiny orange flames. Then the orange flames spread to the dry old tree. In a moment smoke came out of the owl's door.

Mr. Red Head flew to Mrs. Frisky's door and hammered just as hard as he could. Tick-tack, tick-tack! It was the loudest noise he had ever made.

It woke Mrs. Frisky, who rushed to the door, scolding and complaining.

But when she got there, she was too frightened to scold. She saw smoke coming out of the hole where the owl lived. She knew that her own home would be full of smoke in a minute.

She rushed inside and shook her babies to wake them. She pushed them through the doorway and led them to a limb of another tree close by.

Too-oo, the owl, was still away in the forest, hunting for a new home. But when she saw the smoke, she came flying back to find out what was happening.

Just then orange flames roared up the trunk and limbs of the dry old tree.

Mrs. Frisky and the owl were afraid the flames would spread over the whole forest. But then it began to sprinkle.

First it sprinkled, and then rain poured down. It poured and poured so hard that it soon put out the flames.

"The flames are out, and the fire can't spread," Mrs. Frisky called to Mr. Red Head, who was sitting on a limb nearby. "Thank you for saving us from the smoke and flames.

"You are the best neighbor in the whole world, and I hope you'll always be our neighbor."

That evening the owl found a tree where they could all make their homes.

After that Mr. Red Head's noise never bothered Too-oo or Mrs. Frisky. When they heard his tick-tack, they would say, "There's Mr. Red Head, the best neighbor in the whole world."

The Story of White Satin

Once upon a time there was a white pony who was as smooth and shiny as satin, and so he was called White Satin.

He lived on Gay Farm, and every morning he took Farmer Gay's little girl for a ride in a fancy red cart.

"I am the most beautiful pony in the world," he thought as he trotted along, drawing the red cart behind him. "No other pony is so smooth and shiny."

He was a very foolish fellow, always thinking about himself.

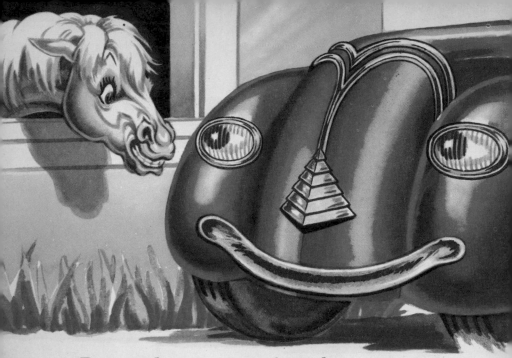

But early one morning the pony saw
something new outside his barn.

It was smooth and shiny, too. It was
as blue as the sky, and it was trimmed
with silver bands. It was a beautiful
blue and silver automobile.

When he saw it, the foolish pony
became very cross.

He put his ears back, showed his
teeth, stamped his feet, and began to
grumble to himself.

When Farmer Gay's little girl came into the yard, she didn't even look at White Satin. She just looked at the sky-blue car and said, "Oh, Father, isn't it beautiful!"

The pony was very angry. "How can she call that ugly car beautiful?" he scolded, stamping his feet and showing his teeth. "I never saw such an ugly thing in all my life.

"I am the one that is beautiful. I am as smooth and shiny as satin."

Then Farmer Gay spoke to his little girl. "Let's take a ride," he said.

The pony thought, "She won't get into that car. She will hitch me to my cart and drive me. I know that she doesn't love that ugly car. She loves me."

But he was wrong. Farmer Gay's little girl did get into the sky-blue car with her father, and away they rode.

"They didn't even speak to me," grumbled the pony. "They don't love me any more. I won't stand it. I'll run away, and then they'll be sorry."

White Satin was as cross as he could be. He waited until evening. As soon as he had eaten his supper, the foolish pony ran out of the barn and galloped away. No one saw him go.

He galloped by the pasture and came to the bottom of a hill. There he saw a pond. He wanted a drink, and so he leaped in.

When he landed in the pond, he made a big splash and woke up the frogs who lived there. They began to make a great noise, all speaking at once.

"Better get out. Better get out," croaked the grandfather frogs in their gruff voices. "Better get out. Better get out!"

"Too deep. Too deep," croaked the father frogs. "Too deep. Too deep!"

"Leap, leap! Leap, leap!" squeaked the little wee frogs in their little high voices. "Leap, leap! Leap, leap!"

White Satin tried to leap, but he couldn't. His feet were stuck fast in the mud at the bottom of the pond. The harder he tried to get out, the deeper he went in. He wasn't able to pull even one foot out of the mud.

Then he heard the frogs again.

"He'll never get out. He'll never get out," croaked the grandfather frogs in their gruff voices.

"Going deeper. Going deeper," croaked the father frogs.

"Too late to leap. Too late to leap," squeaked the little wee frogs.

White Satin was afraid that the frogs were right. His feet were going deeper and deeper into the sticky mud at the bottom of the pond.

The pony wasn't cross now. He was frightened and unhappy. He had never been so unhappy in all his life.

White Satin began to call for help.

After a while a farmer heard him and came to the pond. The man looked at the pony and then ran off. He was going to telephone to Farmer Gay, but the poor unhappy pony didn't know that.

"He isn't going to help me," thought the pony. "He didn't even speak to me."

White Satin felt worse and worse. His feet were going deeper into the mud at the bottom of the pond. The pony was so unhappy that big tears ran down his nose and fell into the water.

The pony got colder and colder and felt worse and worse. The tears kept running down his face.

At last he heard a chug, chug, chug, and a car rolled up to the pond.

He saw Farmer Gay and his little girl in the front seat. In the back seat was the farmer who had found White Satin. Quickly the men got out.

The frogs began croaking again.

"Too late, too late!" they croaked.

"He'll never get out. He'll never get out."

"He's in too deep! He's in too deep!"

"Maybe they're right," thought White Satin, as more tears splashed in the water. "I'll never see my nice, warm barn or my green pasture again."

But Farmer Gay called to him, "Don't be afraid, White Satin. We'll pull you out with the car."

First they threw logs into the mud.
Over the logs they put boards. Then
Farmer Gay walked on the boards and
fastened a rope around the pony. He
tied the other end of the rope to the car.

Then the car backed up and pulled.
At last it drew the pony out of the mud.
His front feet came up on the boards,
and then his hind feet came up.

He was not smooth and shiny now.
He was covered with mud. His teeth
were chattering from the cold, and tears
were running down his face.

The frogs began to croak again.

"Better go home. Better go home."

"And get to bed, and get to bed."

"And go to sleep, and go to sleep."

That was just what poor, tired White Satin wanted to do. But first he went up to the shiny blue and silver car.

He did not speak crossly now or put his ears back or stamp his feet or show his teeth. Instead, he rubbed his nose against the automobile.

Now White Satin loved the sky-blue car. It had saved his life.

Brother Rabbit and Tar Baby

Brother Fox surely did want to catch
Brother Rabbit. He had tried many
different tricks, but in all his life he
had never been able to catch Brother
Rabbit.

One day he thought of a new trick.

He got a wooden doll and a pail of
soft black tar. He put the wooden doll in
the middle of the road and covered it
smoothly with tar from the pail. And so
he made Tar Baby.

"This is the best trick I ever thought
of in my life," he said to himself with
a wicked laugh.

Then Brother Fox hid in some bushes close by. He waited and watched.

By and by Brother Rabbit came down the road. Hippety-hop, hippety-hop-hop! When he saw Tar Baby, he stood right up on his hind legs in surprise.

Then he spoke to Tar Baby. "Good morning!" he said. "Nice weather we're having."

Tar Baby didn't say a word.

"Is that any way to behave?" scolded Brother Rabbit. "I spoke to you, and you had better speak to me. Can't you hear what I'm saying? If you can't, I'll talk a little louder."

Tar Baby didn't say a word.

"You're stuck up. That's what you are," shouted Brother Rabbit. "Speak to me, or I'll hit you. And I can hit hard. Now are you going to speak?"

Tar Baby didn't say a word.

"I'll teach you a lesson you won't forget," said foolish Brother Rabbit, raising his left front foot and hitting Tar Baby.

Of course his foot stuck in the tar, and he couldn't get it loose.

"Let me loose," said Brother Rabbit. "If you don't, I'll hit you again, you stuck-up fellow!"

Tar Baby didn't say a word. So the rabbit hit Tar Baby with his right front foot. And of course that foot stuck, too.

Then he hit Tar Baby with both his hind feet, and they stuck. Last of all, he bumped his head hard against Tar Baby. And his head stuck, too.

Brother Fox came out from the bushes, prancing along as pleased as could be. He surely was enjoying himself.

"Good morning," he said. "So you think that my Tar Baby is stuck up. It seems to me you're the one that's stuck up. All stuck up with tar."

And he began to laugh a wicked laugh. "Ha, ha, ha! Ho, ho, ho!"

He laughed so hard that he rolled on the ground, and the tears ran down his face. He surely was enjoying himself.

"Oh, kind Brother Fox!" begged the poor rabbit. "Please pull me loose."

"Oh, no!" said the wicked old fox. "I won't pull you loose. I'll cook you, and I'll roast you, and I'll eat you for my dinner!"

"Oh, kind Brother Fox," begged the rabbit, with tears in his eyes. "Please don't eat me. Eat something else instead."

"I don't want anything else," said the wicked old fox. "I can hardly wait for my first bite of roast rabbit. M-m!"

The fox raked a big pile of leaves close to Brother Rabbit. He threw logs on the pile and started a fire to cook the rabbit.

As the fire burned, Brother Rabbit got hotter and hotter. He had never been so hot in all his life. He turned and twisted, and twisted and turned, trying to get away from the flames.

Suddenly Brother Rabbit felt his head pulling loose from Tar Baby. The hot fire was making the tar soft.

Then Brother Rabbit had a bright idea. He thought, "My head is already loose. Maybe I can pull my feet loose, too, if the tar grows softer. But first I'll get rid of the fox, so that he won't see me."

So he began to grumble and scold. "Brother Fox," he said, "you can't roast a rabbit with this fire. You need a great big fire instead of this little one."

"All right," said the fox. "I'll bring more logs and make the biggest fire you ever saw. I'll roast you nice and brown."

As soon as Brother Fox had pranced off, Brother Rabbit began to twist and turn some more. He twisted and turned, and turned and twisted until he pulled his hind feet loose.

And when his hind feet were loose, he twisted and turned, and turned and twisted until he pulled his front feet loose.

Hippety-hop! Hippety-hop! Away he ran from the smoke and flames. He hid in some bushes, where he felt safe.

"Ha, ha, ha!" he called out. "I have spoiled your plans, Brother Fox. Build your fire big and hot, but what will you have to cook? You can cook, and you can roast, but you won't have roast rabbit for dinner!"

And off went Brother Rabbit to his home. Hippety-hop, hippety-hop!

He surely was enjoying himself.

Paddy's Christmas

One winter day Paddy Bear hid behind a tree and watched some children in a log cabin at the foot of the mountain.

The little bear saw exciting things and heard exciting things and smelled exciting things. The children in the log cabin were having Christmas, and they were very happy and gay.

Paddy Bear heard them call, "Merry Christmas!" to each other.

"So it's Christmas that makes them happy and gay," said Paddy to himself. "I wonder what Christmas is."

He hurried up the mountain to the big, dark cave where he lived.

"What is Christmas?" he asked his father and mother and uncle and aunt.

But the grown-up bears were sound asleep and didn't hear him. Paddy poked them and bumped against them until they woke up.

He said, "The children in the cabin at the foot of the mountain are having Christmas. What is Christmas?"

"I don't know," yawned Father Bear.

"I don't know," yawned Mother Bear.

"We don't know," yawned Aunt Bear and Uncle Bear. "And don't bother us."

And the big bears went back to sleep.

Once more Paddy bumped against the grown-up bears. At last Uncle Bear woke up. "I'll go down the mountain," he said, with a big yawn. "I'll find out what Christmas is."

Down to the foot of the mountain went Uncle Bear. He hid behind the log cabin and listened and looked and sniffed.

Then he went back to the cave and said, "Christmas is evergreen trees and holly and things like that. You get them and trim the house. Then you sing a song, and that is Christmas."

Uncle Bear went back to sleep. But Paddy ran out of the cave and got a little evergreen tree and some holly with red berries on it to trim the cave.

The cub put up the tree and nailed the holly on the walls. Then he sang a song and pranced around the cave, and for a while he was happy.

But soon Paddy began to feel that something was wrong. So once more he called the grown-up bears.

When they didn't wake up, the little cub poked them with his paws. First a small poke, then a harder poke.

Then he bumped against them. And the big bears woke up.

"This isn't Christmas," said the little cub, shaking his head. "Uncle Bear must be wrong. Christmas must be something more than evergreens and holly.

"When children have Christmas, they get all sorts of pretty things. They have lots of fun, and they feel good from the inside out.

"The holly and the evergreen tree look pretty, and I'm having lots of fun. But I don't feel good from the inside out."

This time it was Aunt Bear who said she would find out what Christmas is.

Down went Aunt Bear to the cabin at the foot of the mountain. She hid behind the cabin and listened and looked.

When she got back to the cave, she said, "Christmas is getting all sorts of gifts, like toys and things to eat. You play and have a good time. See! I've brought you some gifts, Paddy."

In one big paw she had a string of red berries for Paddy, and in another paw she had a small log full of honey. She gave Paddy the berries and the honey, and then she went back to sleep.

The cub hung the string of berries around his neck. He gobbled up the honey and pranced around the cave. And for a while he was happy.

But soon Paddy began to feel that something was wrong.

He thought and thought about it. At last he called the grown-up bears again. When they didn't wake up, Paddy poked them with his paws and bumped against them. At last he woke the big bears.

Paddy said, "I am puzzled. This isn't Christmas. Aunt Bear must be wrong. Christmas must be something more than getting presents.

"When children have Christmas, they get all sorts of pretty things. They have lots of fun, and they feel good from the inside out.

"The string of red berries is pretty, and the honey tasted good. I'm having lots of fun, but I don't feel good from the inside out."

Then Mother Bear said that she would find out what Christmas is.

Down went Mother Bear to the cabin at the foot of the mountain. She hid behind the cabin for a long time and looked and listened and sniffed.

When she got back to the cave, she said, "I have found out what Christmas is! It is more than evergreen trees and holly with pretty red berries. And it is more than getting presents. It is doing something to make someone else happy."

Then she went to sleep again, and at once Paddy ran to the woods.

Soon he came prancing back to the cave. His paws were loaded with all sorts of gifts for the grown-up bears.

Once more Paddy poked and bumped the grown-up bears until he woke them.

"Merry Christmas!" Paddy shouted, as he gave them their gifts. He gave Mother Bear a big bunch of evergreen branches to clean the cave with. He gave Father Bear a stick to lean on when he climbed the mountain.

Paddy's gift to Uncle Bear was a big sack of nuts. And for Aunt Bear he had three red feathers in a basket.

Then Paddy knew that it was really Christmas, for he felt good from the inside out.

The Basket of Laughs

Once upon a time a little old woman and a little old man lived in a little old house on a high hill.

In the big tree outside the house lived a mischievous fairy named Puckity. He could see the woman and her husband, but they couldn't see him. They didn't know that they had a fairy for a neighbor —a mischievous little fairy who enjoyed playing all sorts of tricks.

Every morning at eight o'clock the little old man went down the steep hill with his rake and hoe and shovel. He went down to work in his garden.

Every morning at half past eight the little old woman put on her clean purple dress and a clean white cap and apron. Then she went down the steep hill to do her errands in the village.

One day, as mischievous little Puckity watched her start down the steep hill, he thought, "I'll just follow the old woman. Maybe I can play a joke on her."

Down the steep hill went the little old woman, with a basket on her arm. She was going to the village to buy some groceries and a hen to cook for dinner. In the basket she had a big blue cloth to cover the food.

Mischievous Puckity flew behind her, but of course she did not know it.

In the village the little old woman bought a hen to cook for dinner. She bought some groceries, too—potatoes, apples, oranges, a cabbage, a pound of butter, some bread, and a pot of jam.

The storekeeper put all the food in her basket.

After that the old woman bought a big pillow. She set the basket down and tried to crowd the pillow into it. She leaned over and pushed the pillow and poked it. But she could not get the pillow into the basket.

"I need a bigger basket instead of this one," she said.

So the storekeeper sold her his very biggest basket. She put all her things in it and spread the blue cloth on top.

Then she started up the steep hill, and Puckity flew along. The day was hot and kept getting hotter.

"Dear me!" said the old woman after a while. "What a heavy load I have."

When mischievous Puckity heard her, he had a bright idea. Quickly he flew down to her shoulder, leaned over, and whispered something in her ear.

"What a good idea!" she cried. "I'll get rid of these heavy things and come back for them when it isn't so hot."

She took out the potatoes and oranges and laid them in the shade of a bush.

She went farther up the steep hill. Still her load felt heavy. So she set the basket down, took out the other things, and laid them in the shade of a big rock.

On went the woman. "Dear me!" she complained. "I still feel tired. I'd like to stop and rest in the shade myself."

Once more Puckity leaned over her shoulder and whispered in her ear.

"What a bright idea!" said the woman. "It's lucky my basket is empty. I can lie down in it and take a little rest."

She set the basket on a flat rock in the shade and climbed into it. Then she laid her head on the pillow, covered herself with the cloth, and went to sleep.

With a mischievous smile Puckity watched the old woman.

Late that day, as the sun was setting, her husband came up the hill past the flat rock. When he saw the basket with the blue cloth, he said, "Why, that must be my wife's basket of food on the rock. I'll take it home for her."

He laid down his rake and shovel and hoe and picked up the basket instead. He didn't look under the cloth where his wife was fast asleep.

Puckity spoke some magic words that made the load feel light. So the old woman's husband climbed up the steep hill, carrying the basket over his arm.

And mischicvous Puckity sat on the basket, but of course the old man did not know it.

When the little old man reached his house, he went inside and set the basket down. Then he called to his wife.

How surprised he was when she sat up in the basket! He laughed until the tears ran down his face.

When the old woman found out that her husband had carried her home in the basket, she laughed until the tears ran down her face, too.

And mischievous little Puckity peeped through the window and laughed, too.

"Well," said the little old man, "I thought I was bringing home a basket of food. But instead I brought home a basket of laughs."

Animals in Town and Country

Skipper and the Black Dog

It was a warm summer night, and Skipper was in his own little house in the back yard.

Just that day the puppy had come to live with Bill Page. After supper Bill had put him in his little house and told him to lie down and sleep.

But Skipper didn't lie down and go to sleep. He was unhappy because he was all alone.

He began to cry, making sad little sounds. He hoped that someone would come out of the big house where the Page family lived. But nobody came.

At last the puppy trotted out of his house and looked around.

The big, round moon was high in the sky. It made the back yard almost as light as day.

There were strange shadows and strange sounds and strange smells in the yard. Skipper wanted to find out about them. So he trotted across the yard in the bright moonlight.

All of a sudden he thought he saw a small black dog crossing the yard just ahead of him.

"Arf, arf, arf," barked Skipper, with a friendly wag of his tail. Here was a playmate for him!

Quick as a wink Skipper jumped at the black dog. And quick as a wink the other dog jumped away.

"Arf, arf," barked Skipper. He was very much excited at having a playmate.

"Skipper, behave yourself!" Bill called from the porch. "Be quiet!"

"Arf, arf!" barked Skipper.

Then Bill spoke to the puppy again. "Go and lie down, Skipper," he called. "Lie down and go to sleep!"

So Skipper turned around to go back to his little house. Now he couldn't see the black dog, and he was much puzzled. He didn't understand how he could have lost the black dog in the bright moonlight.

For a while he ran around sniffing, and then he began barking again.

190

"Be quiet, Skipper!" Bill called again from the porch. "Go and lie down."

Skipper turned toward the porch, and again he saw the black dog. It had been behind him all the time.

Quick as a wink he scampered after the black dog, and quick as a wink it scampered away.

Skipper leaped at the other dog again, but still he couldn't reach it. He was puzzled and couldn't understand what was the matter.

Then he began to growl at the other dog and chase it. He chased it all over the yard, but he couldn't catch it.

"Poor puppy," Bill said, "I suppose you don't like to be alone. I'll take you into the house, and you can lie on an old pillow by my bed. Maybe you'll be quiet then."

He ran into the yard to get Skipper.

Just then Skipper hit at the black dog
with one of his little paws. He barked,
and he growled.

Bill looked up at the big moon in the
sky and then down at Skipper. And he
began to laugh.

"Now I understand why you have been
barking and growling," he said, picking
up his pet.

"You have made the funniest mistake
a puppy ever made. You thought you
were chasing another dog, but instead,
you were chasing your shadow in the
moonlight. Just your own black shadow."

Fluffytail and the Peanut Hunt

A Joke on Bill

Fluffytail was a squirrel that lived in Grandmother Page's big front yard.

One morning he looked down from the limb of an oak tree and chattered and chattered. He was excited because he saw Bill hiding peanuts in the yard.

Fluffytail wanted those peanuts! But he didn't dare to go down because Bill's dog was there. If he went down, the dog would chase him.

He watched as Bill hid peanuts here and there and everywhere. He hid one peanut under a dry leaf, ten or eleven behind a big stone near the porch, and some little piles underneath the bushes. "Ch-ch!" scolded Fluffytail. "Ch-ch!" How he did want those peanuts!

Bill didn't even look at the squirrel. He was much too busy hiding peanuts.

That afternoon Grandmother Page was going to give a surprise party for Bill's sister Ellen. It was her fifth birthday. All of her playmates were going to be guests at the party.

One of the games was to be a peanut hunt, and that was why Bill was hiding peanuts.

When Bill had finished, he put on his roller skates and went out of the gate and down the street. Right behind him scampered his frisky little dog.

Now there wasn't any dog to chase Fluffytail. So he scampered down the tree and began to hunt for peanuts.

He found one peanut under a dry leaf and held it tight in his tiny paws while he ate it.

He also found ten or eleven peanuts behind a big stone near the porch and several piles among the bushes.

Here and there and everywhere he found peanuts.

When the squirrel had eaten all he could, he began to dig holes and hide peanuts in the ground. He kept hiding them, one by one, until he had taken all he could find.

At two o'clock Grandmother's big, shady yard was full of guests.

Soon Bill and Ellen came up the street. How surprised Ellen was when she saw all her playmates in the yard and heard them call, "Happy birthday!"

When Bill and Ellen had joined the guests, Grandmother handed each child a paper sack.

"We'll have a peanut hunt," she said. "There is a prize for the one who finds the most peanuts."

"Oh!" cried Lily. "I hope I'll have good luck and find lots of peanuts."

But Lily didn't find lots of peanuts, and nobody else did, either.

Lily found four peanuts under a bush and a fifth one under a dry leaf. Ellen found several among the flowers, and Jay found several more behind a vine. The others didn't find a single peanut.

"I can't understand that," cried Bill. "You ought to find dozens of them. I know where there are ten or eleven."

He ran to a big stone, and several of the other children joined him.

But much to Bill's surprise, there wasn't a single peanut behind the stone. He looked in several other places, but he couldn't find any peanuts.

"Somebody must have taken them," said Lily.

That very moment Bill heard a loud "Ch-ch, ch-ch," from Fluffytail, who was scampering down the oak tree.

"Now I understand!" shouted Bill. "Fluffytail has taken the peanuts."

A Joke on Fluffytail

"Fluffytail spoiled our peanut hunt," laughed Bill. "He played a joke on me, and so I ought to play one on him. I'm going to do it, too."

"How can you?" asked Patty.

"That's a secret," answered Bill, as he went over and whispered something in Grandmother's ear.

While Grandmother took all the guests into the house to play, Bill ran out of the gate. Down the street he dashed, toward a store that sold peanuts.

Then Fluffytail had Grandmother's big yard all to himself, and he began to scamper around among the bushes.

But soon he saw Skipper coming with Bill, and he didn't dare to stay on the ground, because Skipper would chase him. Up the oak tree scampered the squirrel as quick as a wink.

Fluffytail looked down from a limb of
the oak tree and saw Bill with a sack
of peanuts. He was scattering some
of them among the flowers.

"Ch-ch!" chattered Fluffytail. More
peanuts! This was almost too good to
be true.

Very slowly Fluffytail began to come
down the oak tree. A little farther, and
a little farther. He had almost reached
the ground when Skipper dashed over
to the tree. "Bow-wow-wow!" he said.

And Fluffytail didn't dare to go any
farther. This time he couldn't get a
single peanut. Skipper wouldn't let
him. Now the joke was on Fluffytail.

Fluffytail's Prize

When the sack was empty, Bill rang a bell, and the guests all joined him in the yard.

Then they had another peanut hunt. This time they enjoyed the game. They found peanuts among bushes, behind stones, in a little pile of dry leaves, and in all sorts of other places.

Fluffytail scolded and chattered. He hated to see somebody else getting all the peanuts.

But Skipper was watching him, and he did not dare to go down.

After ten minutes Bill rang a bell and
called, "Now count your peanuts."

All the guests counted their peanuts,
and Lily had a hundred and twenty-nine.
She had the most of all.

So Grandmother handed her the prize.
It was a story book.

"Oh, what a nice prize!" said Lily.
"But Fluffytail ought to get a prize, too.
He found the most peanuts of all. I
know the kind of prize he'd like."

She went skipping around the yard,
scattering peanuts from her sack.

Then after the dog and the children
had gone home, Fluffytail had another
peanut hunt all by himself.

Chip, the Baby Chipmunk

Bill Feeds Chip

Sniff, sniff, sniff went Chip, the baby chipmunk. He had just come out from his home underneath a big log, because he smelled food. Somebody was cooking breakfast among the trees nearby.

Chip wanted some of that breakfast himself, but his mother had taught him to be careful. She had taught him to keep away from people.

So he didn't go any closer. He just
sat up and watched the Page family.

They had come to the forest the day
before. Since then they had done all
sorts of strange things that Chip didn't
understand. They had put up a tent and
taken bags and boxes out of the car.

Now Mrs. Page was baking corn meal
pancakes at the big stone fireplace.

Chip forgot that his mother had taught
him to be careful, and he went closer.

All of a sudden Bill pointed to Chip and shouted, "Look at that chipmunk!"

With one frightened squeak, the little fellow dashed into his hole.

"It's too bad I scared him," said Bill. "He'd be a fine pet to take home. I wonder if I can tame him while we're on our vacation."

"Maybe you can tame him," said Mr. Page. "Next time you see him, don't move and don't make any noise."

"Perhaps he'd be as easy to tame as Fluffytail," said Bill. "I've just taught the squirrel to eat out of my hand, and maybe I can teach this chipmunk, too. I'll begin right now."

Bill walked to the log and held out several bits of corn meal pancake and a piece of orange.

"I wish he'd come and get it," thought Bill. But Chip didn't come.

At last Bill scattered the food on
the ground. Chip peeped out at the bits
of pancake and the piece of orange.
Oh, but they smelled good!

He had never had anything to eat
but weed seeds, nuts, and other things
he found in the forest. Chip wanted
this strange new food very much.

But he had been taught to keep away
from people. So he didn't dare to come
out of his hole until the boy had gone
into the tent.

Then the little chipmunk became brave
enough to scamper over to the food.

Chip sat up on his hind legs, held the piece of orange between his tiny front paws, and began to eat it. How good the orange tasted!

Then he nibbled the bits of corn meal pancake which were scattered on the ground. When he had eaten them all, he scampered back to his hole.

That was Monday morning. All day Monday and all day Tuesday Chip kept finding food scattered near the log. Bits of apple and orange and other fruit. And also a big cabbage leaf.

Chip ate everything—even a bit of boiled potato. He wasn't afraid now.

Little by little he was getting tame.

Chip and the Chocolate Cookies

By Tuesday evening Chip became so brave that he even dared to climb on the table near the tent. And he found a cardboard box of chocolate cookies that somebody had laid on the table.

Chip gnawed a hole in the cardboard box with his sharp teeth and began to nibble the chocolate cookies. He was so busy nibbling them that he did not hear Bill coming.

"Oh!" cried Bill. "So you're nibbling our chocolate cookies! Now I know how to set a trap for you."

Bill's voice scared Chip. With a frightened squeak, the little chipmunk rushed straight home.

But the next morning Chip felt brave again. Back he came and found the same box of chocolate cookies.

If he had stopped to look, he would have seen a bigger wooden box above it. The wooden box was held up by a stick that had a string fastened to it.

This was the trap that Bill had made. If the stick was pulled out, the empty wooden box would fall down over the cardboard box.

The chipmunk didn't notice that Bill was nearby, ready to pull the string. He didn't know there was any danger. So he went right up to the cardboard box.

Before he could take a single nibble, Bill pulled the string. Crash! The stick fell. Then down crashed the big box. Chip was caught in Bill's trap.

Ellen, who was in the tent, heard the crash and ran to look at the chipmunk.

With frightened squeaks, he dashed back and forth in the wooden box.

"Bill," begged Ellen, "please let the chipmunk go. He'd like to be free."

"Oh, no!" answered Bill. "He'll soon be tame, and we'll have a fine pet to take home from our vacation."

So Bill kept Chip in the box all day.

That evening about nine o'clock, when nobody was stirring about or making any noise, Mother Chipmunk joined her baby on the table. At once she began to gnaw the wood with her sharp teeth.

Inside the box Chip started to gnaw with his sharp teeth. Both chipmunks gnawed and gnawed. But gnawing that wooden box was slow work.

The noise woke Bill, who was asleep in the tent. In the moonlight he could see brave Mother Chipmunk gnawing at the box to set her baby free. When she heard somebody stirring, she dashed off.

But Chip kept gnawing at the box.

"I hate to give him up," thought Bill. "He'd be a fine pet, but he'd like to be free. Probably I ought to let him go."

Then Bill lifted the wooden box, and quick as a wink Chip dashed away. In a few seconds he was safe in his home.

Salt for the Deer

The Deer in the Meadow

Early one morning Mother Deer led her two babies quietly through the green forest until they came to a wide, sunny meadow. For a moment they all stood very still.

Then Mother Deer left the two babies in the shadows among the trees and stepped out alone into the sunlight.

211

Mother Deer had sharp eyes and sharp ears. She looked all around and listened carefully. She wanted to see if there were any signs of danger.

But she couldn't see or hear or smell any fierce wild animals that might hurt her babies. So she crossed the meadow to a pool of water and began to drink.

The fawns never stirred from their place in the shadows until their mother wagged her tail as a signal for them to come. Then they pranced across the meadow and went to the pool for a drink of water.

While the fawns were drinking, their mother raised her head. Again she listened for any signs of danger.

For a while the only sounds were the singing of wrens, the screaming of a bluejay, and the cawing of a crow that was in a tree near the pool.

Suddenly there was a loud sneeze behind a bush where the whole Page family were hiding. They were watching the doe and her two fawns.

The moment Mother Deer heard that sneeze, she signaled to the fawns and dashed into the forest. The fawns were close behind her. In a few seconds all three deer were out of sight.

"Oh," said Bill, "it's too bad that I sneezed and frightened the deer."

"You couldn't help sneezing," said Mother. "And anyway, they'll probably come back tomorrow."

"Will they?" said Bill. "Well, if the deer come here every day to drink, I might be able to tame the fawns and have them for pets."

"Now, Bill," laughed his father, "just remember Chip. Do you want to trap the fawns?"

"No," said Bill. "I know that would be a foolish thing to do! Chip taught me a lesson. I want the fawns to be free, but I'd like to tame them while we're on our vacation."

"Why don't you put salt on their tails," laughed Ellen. "I've heard of catching birds that way."

"That's not such a joke as you seem to think," said Father. "Probably we can tame the fawns with salt. All deer love salt. The storekeeper in town has some blocks of salt. I'll buy a block on Monday when I go to town."

How Bill Tamed the Deer

On Monday afternoon Mr. Page bought a block of salt. Monday evening he set it out in the meadow for the deer.

When the doe and her fawns visited the meadow early Tuesday morning, Mother Deer noticed the big block of salt right away. She went over and sniffed at it, while the fawns waited in the shadows.

The Page family were hiding among the bushes. They enjoyed watching the beautiful animals. But Bill forgot that he ought to be quiet and began to speak.

That spoiled everything. Quick as a wink the doe leaped away from the salt block and dashed off, with her babies close behind her.

Bill waited all Tuesday morning to see if the deer would come back, but he didn't see them again that day.

Next morning the three deer visited the meadow again, and this time the doe signaled her fawns to join her at the salt block.

Bill was watching from the bushes, but he didn't stir, and Mother Deer did not notice that anybody was there.

The doe and her fawns stayed about twenty minutes and licked the salt block with their pink tongues.

Then Bill had an idea. He made up his mind that each night he would move the block of salt a little nearer to the tent.

So every night for the rest of the week Bill moved the block of salt a little bit nearer to the tent.

And the deer didn't seem to mind. They would go to the block of salt and lick it with their long pink tongues.

"The deer are getting tame already," said Bill. "They're not afraid to come near the tent.

"Next week is the last week of our vacation. But probably I can still tame them if I hurry up. On Monday I'll let them see me."

So on Monday Bill didn't hide. When the three deer crossed the meadow, he was sitting on the ground near the block of salt. He sat as still as a stone.

To Bill's great joy, the doe and her fawns didn't run away. But they would not come close to Bill. They just stood still and looked at him and at the salt.

Bill was in sight again on Tuesday when the deer came to the meadow. He sat just as near the block of salt as he had on Monday.

The doe looked at him with her big eyes. Slowly she went over to the block of salt and began to lick it.

She watched Bill. When he didn't stir, she wagged her tail as a signal to the fawns, and they came prancing across the meadow and joined her.

One fawn began to nibble some grass, while the other one sniffed at Bill's leg.

Bill wanted to shout with joy, but he did not move or make a sound. He hardly dared to take a breath.

"The deer are almost tame now!" he thought. "Tomorrow I'll hold some salt in my hand and see what they'll do. Probably they'll run away, but I'd like to try it before our vacation is over."

The next morning Bill held a piece of salt and waited without stirring.

Soon the doe and her fawns came out of the shadows and crossed the meadow.

To Bill's joy, one fawn put out its tongue and licked the salt in his hand. Finally the other fawn licked it, too.

"They are both tame," thought Bill. "They're tame, and yet they're free!"

When the deer had gone, Mother, Father, and Ellen came out from the tent, where they had been watching.

"You did tame the fawns with salt," cried Ellen. "Only you put the salt on their tongues instead of on their tails!"

The Bears' Picnic

With a push of her big, strong paw, Mother Bear turned a log over and uncovered hundreds of bugs. There were hundreds and hundreds of bugs.

Mother Bear and her two little cubs gobbled the bugs very fast.

A wren and a woodpecker flew down. They wanted to eat some bugs, too, but they didn't have a chance to get any.

In a minute the bears had eaten the bugs. Mother Bear gave a low grunt and waddled off. The cubs followed her.

Soon Mother Bear noticed some bushes that were full of berries. She began to gobble the juicy berries as fast as she could. The cubs watched her for a moment, and then they began to eat the juicy berries, too.

When the berries were gone, Mother Bear stood up on her hind legs and began to sniff.

The cubs also stood up and began to sniff. There were wonderful, wonderful smells in the air.

With a low grunt, Mother Bear started off, and the cubs followed her.

Soon they saw something that made their mouths water. A picnic lunch was spread out on a paper tablecloth! There were cups of milk and plates of food.

The Page family were just sitting down to lunch. Their vacation was over, and they were on their way home. They had to be back by Monday.

Bill sat down and picked up a plate. "I'm as hungry as a bear," he said.

Just then Mr. Page looked up and saw the three bears coming toward them.

"Jump in the car! Quick!" he cried.

They jumped into their automobile and watched the bears through the windows.

The cubs knocked over the paper cups. They grabbed sandwiches and hard-boiled eggs from the paper plates and gobbled them up as fast as they could.

Mother Bear saw some cup cakes covered with thick white frosting. She grabbed two of the cup çakes and tried to eat both of them at once.

This was the first chance she had ever had to eat cake, and how she did enjoy herself! Mother Bear got frosting on her paws, frosting on her mouth, and frosting on her neck. It stuck to her fur and made her look very funny.

"How would you like to tame those bears, Bill?" laughed Ellen.

"Well," said Bill, "if we were just starting on our vacation, I might try."

One cub found a tall can of chocolate cookies. He put his head in and ate and ate until the can was empty.

When he had eaten all the cookies, he tried to pull his head out. But it was stuck tight in the empty can.

He raised his head and twisted and turned it, but the cookie can wouldn't come off.

Finally, when Mother Bear had licked the frosting from her paws, she waddled over to her cub. Bang, bang! She hit the tin can twice, and away it flew.

"Bears are the funniest animals in the world!" laughed Bill.

Then one cub licked some frosting from a plate. In and out went his pink tongue as he licked the plate clean.

The other cub grabbed a glass of jam and licked the glass clean.

Soon the bears had taken every bit of food—sandwiches, fruit, cookies, and the cup cakes with thick frosting. Even hard-boiled eggs, shells and all, and half a dozen juicy oranges.

When the bears ran off, Mother Bear still had spots of frosting on her fur.

"This has been a wonderful end to our vacation," said Bill.

"Yes," laughed Mother, "but we can't have lunch until we reach the next town. The bears have taken everything but the cups and plates and the jam glass."

Bill said, "That's all right. I thought I was as hungry as a bear. But I'm not as hungry as those bears were."

Ringtail, the Young Raccoon

Ringtail Sees the World

Ringtail wanted to go down the big tree. Down to the ground below.

He was a young raccoon with thick, dark fur and a fine bushy tail. Ringtail lived with his family in a hole in the trunk of the tree.

Little Sister was in the hole now, fast asleep. She would sleep until Mother and Father Raccoon came home with food.

Here was Ringtail's chance to go and see the strange world below.

So the furry little fellow started down the tree. Nobody had ever taught him to climb down a tree, but he knew just what to do.

He hung on tight to the bark of the tree with his sharp nails and moved along carefully.

Down, down he went toward the ground below. It seemed like a long way, but finally he reached the bottom of the tree.

Ringtail looked around. All about him were tall weeds and bushes and big trees.

He started out bravely to see the world.

What strange sounds there were—the fierce squawk of a bird, the swishing of branches, the croaking of frogs. Now Ringtail was beginning to be afraid.

When he had gone a little farther, he heard a crash of thunder. Twice more he heard loud crashes of thunder.

Ringtail did not feel very brave now. He didn't go one step farther. Back to his tree he dashed and up the trunk, twice as fast as he had come down.

Ringtail popped into his hole just as there was another crash of thunder. And the little raccoon didn't stir out of his home again that night. He didn't want to see any more of the strange world just then.

Ringtail Goes Fishing

One evening several weeks later, the two young raccoons were taken on a fishing trip by their father and mother.

Just as the big, round moon began to shine, the raccoons started for the river.

Father Raccoon led his family through the thick grass and the bushes. The moon made queer-looking shadows in the forest, and the air was full of strange night sounds.

But this time Ringtail was not afraid, and Little Sister was not afraid, either. The little raccoons were sure that their mother and father would take good care of them.

They traveled along until they reached
the river bank. Then Father Raccoon
gave his children a fishing lesson. He
walked into the water and felt around
on the sandy bottom with his front paws.

Soon he came back with something
in his mouth. It looked like a round
stone, but it really was a shell.

Father Raccoon had seen shells like
that before. He knew that if he pulled
the shell apart, he would find a juicy
clam inside.

Sure enough! When he pulled it apart,
there was a nice, juicy clam.

Little Sister tried to grab the clam, but Father Raccoon kept it and swished it around in the water. He was showing Little Sister how to wash the clam, for raccoons like to wash their food.

When Father Raccoon had taught Little Sister how to wash the clam, he gave it to her. The furry baby grabbed it and popped it into her mouth.

Then Mother Raccoon found a clam and pulled the shell apart. Ringtail quickly grabbed that clam and washed it and popped it into his mouth.

When Ringtail and Little Sister had eaten several clams, Ringtail wanted to catch a big, juicy one for himself.

So he walked bravely into the river and felt around on the sandy bottom of the stream. He was in a great hurry and moved his paws over the bottom of the stream as fast as he could.

All at once Ringtail began to cry out. One of his paws was caught. He had put it inside a clam shell that was open, and quick as a wink the shell had closed up tight! The clam had caught Ringtail!

The poor little fellow twisted and turned his paw, but he couldn't get it free from the clam shell.

With a loud cry, Ringtail started for the bank of the stream.

Little Sister and the two grown-up raccoons came running to see what was the matter.

Ringtail hopped out of the stream on three legs and held up the paw with the clam shell on it.

Father Raccoon took hold of the shell and began to pull it apart. In just a moment he had pulled the shell apart, and Ringtail's paw was free.

Then the little raccoon lay down on the bank of the stream and licked his paw. It hurt, but after he had licked it a while, it began to feel better.

Little Sister caught some clams. She pulled the shells apart and washed the clams. Then she popped the juicy clams into her mouth.

Soon Ringtail was back in the stream, bravely catching clams, too. This time he didn't make the mistake of moving his paws too fast. He caught several juicy clams, but he didn't let any more clams catch him.

Paddle Tail

Paddle Tail and his twin sister, Water Baby, swam out of the doorway of their house in the big pool. They were right behind Mother Beaver, and they followed her to the top of the pool.

The beaver twins splashed and swam, and swam and splashed, and had a fine time in the deep pool. They swam down into the water and slowly up to the top again.

The water was as smooth as glass, and the sun was warm and pleasant on their smooth, furry backs.

234

All at once there was a noise among the trees, and some people came out of the woods.

Mother Beaver was frightened. She lifted up her thick, flat tail and then brought it down on the water with a hard slap.

When the beaver twins heard the slap, they dived straight down into the pool and hid in their house. Mother Beaver dived down and hid, too.

That slapping noise is the beaver's danger signal. No beaver makes such a noise unless danger is near.

For a while the three beavers stayed in their house and hid. But finally Mother Beaver swam back to the top of the pool and let Paddle Tail and Water Baby join her.

One by one the three brown heads bobbed up to the top of the water.

Soon Mother Beaver swam over to the shore of the pool and called to the twins to join her. She led them away from the shore and into the forest.

All of a sudden she smelled a wolf. Quickly she pushed the little beavers into the shadows behind a thick, bushy vine. They stayed there without stirring.

Just then a fawn dashed past them. Close behind it came a fierce gray wolf. Oh, how frightened the beavers were!

They saw the fawn make a quick turn and get away, but the wolf was going so fast that he kept straight on. He didn't notice the beavers.

Mother Beaver and her twins were safe, but they were shaking with fright.

The three beavers waited quietly for
several minutes, and then they hurried
farther into the green forest.

To the joy of the little beavers, they
soon came to the shore of a large pond
where there were several beaver houses.
Some young beavers were playing on a
log not far from shore.

Paddle Tail and his sister watched
the strangers dive into the deep water.
The twins watched the smooth brown
heads bob up again as the strangers
swam to the top of the pond.

Paddle Tail could hardly wait for a chance to join these new playmates on the log.

The beaver twins did not have any playmates in their own pool, because no other beaver families lived there.

When Mother Beaver dived into the water, her two furry babies quickly followed her.

They swam straight over to the log where the strangers were playing.

They climbed up on it, and then they, too, dived into the pond and came bobbing up again. It was fun to splash around with their new playmates.

All of a sudden Paddle Tail noticed something moving among the trees on the shore. He thought he could see the gray fur of a wolf. The animal was not far away from some big beavers that were on the shore of the pond.

Unless they dived into the water,
those big beavers would be in danger
from the wolf.

Slap! In his fright the little beaver
brought his flat tail down on the water
as hard as he could.

As soon as he had given the danger
signal, he dived into the pond quick
as a wink.

The other beavers heard the danger
signal. They all dived out of sight—
Paddle Tail's mother and sister, his new
playmates, and also the big beavers
on the shore.

It was a good thing Paddle Tail had noticed the wolf and given the danger signal. The fierce gray animal had been very close to the big beavers on the shore.

For a while the beavers did not come back to the top of the pond. But finally they got over their fright, and one by one their smooth brown heads came bobbing up to the top of the water.

They looked about them carefully, but their enemy had gone.

Paddle Tail and Water Baby bobbed up, too, and joined their playmates on the log. They dived into the cool pond and bobbed up to the top again. Down and up, and down and up.

What a joy it was for the beaver twins to splash in the pond with their new playmates!

Chuckle Makes a Friend

One summer day Chuckle lay in the sunshine on a stone wall. He was a fat, furry young ground hog who loved to lie in the sun.

Nearby, Chuckle's mother was nibbling at an ear of corn. Suddenly she dropped it and gave a loud whistle.

Chuckle knew very well that her loud whistle was a danger signal. Mother Ground Hog never whistled that way unless danger was near.

Chuckle knew he should run home, but he wanted to see what the danger was.

He didn't have to wait long. In a moment he saw a large dog. Chuckle jumped up in fright and popped into his hole under the stone wall.

His mother dashed after him. The big dog was already so close that his sharp teeth almost caught her tail.

With an angry growl, the dog poked his nose between the rocks. He growled and growled, but he couldn't reach the ground hogs.

Chuckle never forgot the fright the dog had given him. So when he was old enough to have a home of his own, he made a deep hole under a tree. There he would be safe from dogs. He knew that they were his enemies and would hurt him if they could.

He made his home beside a clover field where he could get food. And near the clover field there was a stream where he could get water to drink.

One morning when Chuckle was asleep in his hole, a clap of thunder woke him.

It thundered and thundered, and rain poured down, but he went back to sleep.

All day the rainstorm kept up, and late in the afternoon water began to pour into Chuckle's home. Then he woke up and rushed to his doorway to see what was the matter.

It had rained so much that there was a flood. The stream had already spread over the clover field. And the storm was still keeping up.

Chuckle knew he would not be safe unless he went to a place high enough to be above the water.

Finally Chuckle started out for a high rock in the middle of the clover field. He could probably reach that rock, and if he got there, he would be safe from the flood.

Chuckle hated to go through the storm and the flood. But he had to get to that rock.

So off he went in the storm, with the thunder crashing and the rain pouring down. At first he splashed along in the water, and then he swam.

When Chuckle finally reached the rock, his thick brown fur was wet and muddy. He was so tired that he could hardly climb up. Twice he went sliding down the steep sides and fell back into the water.

But at last he reached the top of the rock. And then he stopped in fright. There was one of his enemies, a dog!

Chuckle looked closer and saw that the dog was a puppy about his own size. He did not look like an enemy.

Chuckle was going to stay on that rock, even if he had to fight. But the puppy didn't try to fight. He didn't even growl. He hardly bothered to look at Chuckle.

The puppy and Chuckle stayed on the rock as far apart as they could. All during the night they stayed there, while the flood grew worse and worse.

By morning the water was so deep that only the very top of the rock was uncovered. Now Chuckle and the puppy were not far apart any more. They were not enemies now.

In the morning it stopped raining. Before noon the sun began to shine over the flooded clover field.

But the water did not go down very fast, even after the storm was over. So Chuckle and the puppy stayed on the rock all day and all night.

During the night they drew close together to keep warm. They weren't enemies now.

The next morning the flood had gone down. So the puppy trotted off through the mud to his home, and Chuckle went off and hid in some bushes until his home was dry.

Nearly a year passed by. One spring day Chuckle walked across the clover field to the rock where he had stayed during the flood. He climbed to the top to enjoy the warm spring sun.

Suddenly a dog twice his size jumped on the rock with fierce growls, as if he wanted to fight.

Chuckle stood up, ready to fight an enemy. But the dog stopped growling and began to sniff. Instead of fighting, he wagged his tail with joy.

Chuckle sniffed, too, and then he knew his friend. It was the puppy he had met during the flood. He had grown to be a big dog now—twice the size of Chuckle. But he still wasn't an enemy.

The old friends knew each other after all this time. They lay down on the big rock, and during the afternoon they stayed there and enjoyed the warm sun.

On the Roads
of Long Ago

The Lad and the North Wind

The Magic Tablecloth

A long time ago a lad and his mother lived in a poor little house.

One cold winter day the mother was going to make porridge. So the lad went to get some meal.

As he returned with the meal, along came the North Wind, puffing and blowing. He puffed at the meal with his strong breath and scattered it in the air.

Then the lad became very angry.

"I'll go to the North Wind's home and ask for that meal," he said. "And he'd better give it back to me."

The weather was cold, and the way was long, but at last the lad reached the North Wind's home.

"GOOD DAY!" roared the North Wind in a gruff voice. "What do you want?"

"I want you to give back our meal," said the lad. "We need it for porridge."

"I can't give back your meal," said the North Wind. "I don't have it. But I'll give you this tablecloth instead. It's a very useful cloth. It's worth more than all the meal in the world.

"When you're hungry, just say, 'Cloth, cloth, spread yourself.' Then it will serve you all sorts of good food."

The lad thanked the North Wind for the tablecloth, and started home.

It grew dark early that winter day. So the lad stopped at an inn for the night.

After he had rested a while, he laid the cloth on a table and said, "Cloth, cloth, spread yourself." At once the cloth served dinner. It served hot bread with honey and cheese. It served a roast duck and two roast geese on a big plate.

When the man who kept the inn saw this, he thought, "That cloth would be worth a lot to me."

The wicked innkeeper made up his mind to steal the magic cloth when he had a chance. After the guests were asleep, he took it from under the lad's pillow and left another cloth instead.

In the morning the lad put the cloth in his jacket pocket and went home.

"Look," he said to his mother. "I have traveled to the North Wind's home, and he has given me a magic cloth that is worth more than all the meal in the world. It's a real treasure.

"When I want food, it serves me hot bread with honey and cheese, and it serves me roast ducks and roast geese on a big plate."

"I'll never believe that unless I see it," said his mother.

So the boy laid the cloth on a table and said, "Cloth, cloth, spread yourself." But the cloth did not serve a bit of food.

253

The lad returned to the North Wind. "Good day, North Wind!" he called.

"GOOD DAY," roared the North Wind in his gruff voice. "What do you want now?"

"I want my meal," said the lad. "That cloth you gave me isn't worth a penny. It won't serve me even a piece of cheese or a bit of dry bread."

"I can't give back your meal," said the North Wind. "I don't have it. But I'll give you this magic sheep instead. It's a very useful sheep. It is worth more than all the meal in the world.

"Whenever you need money, just say, 'Sheep, sheep, give money.' Then the sheep will open its mouth, and golden coins will drop out."

The lad thanked the North Wind and went off, leading the sheep by a rope.

That evening the lad went to the same inn, leading his sheep. After he had eaten supper, he said, "Sheep, sheep, give money." The sheep's mouth opened, and golden coins dropped out.

"Golden coins!" cried the other guests. "What a wonderful sheep!"

"Oho!" thought the wicked innkeeper. "That sheep would be worth a lot to me. I'll steal it tonight, and then I can have thousands of golden coins, and I'll be rich."

When all the guests at the inn were asleep, the wicked innkeeper saw his chance to steal the magic sheep. In its place he left another sheep.

The next morning the lad went home, leading the sheep behind him.

"Mother," cried the lad, "look at this sheep the North Wind has given me. It is a real treasure. It is worth more than all the meal in the world. It gives me golden coins when I ask for them."

"I'll never believe that unless I see it," said his mother.

So the lad said, "Sheep, sheep, give money!" But it didn't give one coin.

The Magic Stick

The lad returned to the North Wind and said, "I want my meal. That sheep you gave me isn't worth a penny."

"I can't give back your meal," roared the North Wind. "But I'll give you this magic stick instead.

"If you want to have it beat somebody, just say, 'Beat, stick, beat.' It will keep on beating until you say, 'Stick, stop beating.' It's a very useful stick."

"Oho!" said the lad. "I shall find it useful." For by this time the lad had guessed that the wicked innkeeper had taken his magic cloth and sheep.

That night the lad returned to the inn.

When the innkeeper saw the stick, he felt sure it was a magic one. After the guests were asleep, he crept over to the lad, laid another stick beside him, and snatched the magic stick.

But the lad was only pretending to be asleep. Quickly he cried out, "Beat, stick, beat!"

The stick began to beat the man and kept on beating him until he screamed, "Don't hit me! Don't hit me!"

He ran wildly this way and that. He jumped over tables and chairs, but the stick followed him.

"Save me! Save me!" he called to the lad. "Make your stick stop beating me, and I'll give back your magic cloth and magic sheep. This will be a lesson to me. I'll never steal anything again."

"Stick, stop beating," called the lad, and the stick crashed to the floor.

When the innkeeper had given back the magic cloth and the magic sheep, the lad was happy.

"The North Wind is a good fellow, after all," he thought. "These are very useful gifts he has given us. These gifts are worth a thousand times as much as the meal that the North Wind blew away. They are real treasures."

And so when morning came, the happy lad went home with the magic cloth, the magic sheep, and the magic stick.

The Fairy Shoemaker

Tom Looks for a Pot of Gold

"Mother," cried Tom, "we're going to be rich. The Fairy Shoemaker knows where there is a huge pot of gold, with thousands of coins in it! I'm going to catch him and make him tell me his secret."

Tom's mother smiled and said, "I have heard that the Fairy Shoemaker is a sly elf. I think you'll become rich sooner if you do some useful work and earn your golden coins."

But Tom did not like to work, and so he started to hunt for the elf.

Every day that week Tom hunted for the Fairy Shoemaker in the woods and in the meadows.

At last one afternoon Tom heard a tiny tapping sound.

"Tick-a-tack, tick-a-tack,
Tick-a-tack-too."

At first he thought it was the tapping of a woodpecker, but when he listened closely, he could hear somebody singing softly in a tiny voice,

"Tick-a-tack, tick-a-tack,
Tick-a-tack-too.
Tack a toe, tack a heel.
Soon we'll have a shoe."

Tom crept quietly toward the voice.

"Oho!" he thought. "That must be the song of the Fairy Shoemaker. I'll catch him, and then he'll have to lead me to the huge pot of gold. Soon my mother and I will be rich."

He crept forward quietly on his hands and knees until he could see the Fairy Shoemaker. The tiny elf had a long nose and a pointed chin, and he wore a tall cap and an apron.

The elf was busy pounding tacks into a tiny shoe that was upside down in front of him. As he worked, he sang,

"Tick-a-tack, tick-a-tack,
Tick-a-tack-too.
Tack a toe, tack a heel.
Soon we'll have a shoe."

"Good day," said Tom politely. But the elf pretended that he didn't hear. He never even glanced up.

"Show me the pot of gold," cried Tom.

"Wait a minute," said the elf. "I just dropped a tack. Help me find it."

Tom knew that if he took his eyes off the Fairy Shoemaker, the sly little elf would disappear.

"I'll pretend I'm looking for the tack," thought Tom, "but I won't take my eyes off him, or he'll disappear."

As Tom crept forward on his hands and knees, the sly elf snatched up some dust and threw it in Tom's face. The dust made Tom sneeze, and when he sneezed, he shut his eyes. He opened them quickly, but the elf had disappeared.

Tom Tries Again

Tom was not ready to give up. He said to himself, "If I found the Fairy Shoemaker once, I can find him twice. Next time I won't let him throw dust in my eyes and make me sneeze."

Every day Tom hunted for the elf, and on the fifth day he heard the tap, tap, tap of the Fairy Shoemaker's hammer again. When he listened closely, he could hear the elf singing,

"Tick-a-tack, tick-a-tack,
Tick-a-tack-too.
Tack a toe, tack a heel.
Soon we'll have a shoe."

Tom crept forward until he could see the elf sitting in the shade of a tree.

"Now," thought Tom, "I won't let him throw dust in my face. And I'll keep my eyes on him, so that he can't disappear. I won't glance away once."

The Fairy Shoemaker was pounding tacks into the toe of a tiny shoe that was upside down in front of him.

"That's a fine shoe," said Tom, as he crept forward on his hands and knees.

He kept his eyes on the elf every single minute, so that the little man wouldn't disappear.

"Why do you work so hard?" said Tom.

"We should all work," answered the elf, without glancing up. "You ought to do a little work yourself for a change."

"Ho, ho, ho!" laughed Tom. "That would be foolish. I don't need to work. I'll become rich without working."

And quick as a wink Tom grabbed the Fairy Shoemaker.

"I have caught you at last," cried Tom. "Now you can't throw dust in my eyes and make me sneeze. And I won't let you go unless you lead me to the huge pot of gold."

"Well," said the elf, "if I must lead you to my treasure, I suppose I must."

Away they went across the meadow and into the thick woods.

"You'll find the huge pot of gold there," said the elf, pointing to the foot of a tree. "Dig there for the treasure."

"I'll have to go home for a shovel," said Tom. "But first I'll put my yellow tie around this tree. Then I can find the right tree when I come back."

Tom glanced at the Fairy Shoemaker and saw that he was smiling slyly.

"Will you promise not to touch this tie while I am gone?" asked Tom.

"Yes, I promise not to touch it," said the sly elf. "And I promise not to let anybody else touch it, either."

"Then I'll let you go free," said Tom, putting the Fairy Shoemaker down. "Thanks for leading me to the gold."

The elf began to laugh. "Ho, ho, ho!" he laughed. "You'll find that you have to work for any gold you get."

And pop! The next second he had disappeared.

Tom ran and got a shovel and hurried back to the woods. He could hardly wait to begin digging for the treasure.

"We'll be rich!" he cried with joy. "I caught the Fairy Shoemaker, and he told me his secret."

When Tom returned to the woods, he gave a long, loud whistle of surprise, for every single tree had a yellow tie around it.

The Fairy Shoemaker had kept his promise. Nobody had touched Tom's tie, but the sly elf had fooled him again.

"I can't tell which tie is mine," said Tom, almost in tears. "Now I'll never be able to find the treasure."

Finally Tom turned sadly toward his home. "My mother is right," he said. "I'll become rich sooner if I do some useful work and earn my gold."

The Turtle's Race

One day a turtle was crawling slowly down a path in the shady woods. Along came a rabbit, kicking up his heels happily as he ran. He passed the turtle, and then he stopped for a moment.

"Good morning, turtle," said the rabbit. "Where are you going?"

"I am on my way to the river," said the turtle, as he crawled slowly along.

"Ho, ho! Ho, ho!" laughed the rabbit. "You'll never reach the river if you crawl along in that slow way. You ought to try hopping along fast, for a change. That's the way to get to the river in a hurry."

"I can't hop like you," said the turtle. "I can only crawl. But I'll get to the river just the same, and perhaps I'll get there before you do."

"Ho, ho, ho!" laughed the rabbit. "Do you really think that you can beat me? Shall we have a race?"

"I don't mind if we do," answered the turtle. "And maybe I'll win."

Away they went. The turtle crawled slowly along the path, but the rabbit kicked up his heels and hopped so fast that he left the slow turtle far behind.

Then the foolish rabbit made a big mistake. He was tired and out of breath, and so he sat down to rest.

"I'm almost at the river," he said with a yawn. "That slow turtle can't win this race. I'll take a little nap."

The rabbit lay down in the shade of a bush, and soon he was fast asleep.

The turtle kept crawling along. It looked as if he didn't have a chance to win, for the rabbit was so far ahead that he was out of sight.

But the turtle never stopped crawling. He did not get out of breath, and he did not stop to rest. Slowly but surely he crawled along.

After a while he passed the rabbit, who was taking his nap in the shade of a bush.

"Oho, what luck!" said the turtle, with a little chuckle. "When that foolish rabbit wakes up from his nap, he won't think he's so clever. I'll fool him yet."

After a long nap the rabbit woke up. He did not know that the turtle had passed him. So he said with a yawn, "I might as well go to the river and wait for him to come crawling along."

Down to the river he went, kicking up his heels happily. But when he got there, he was so surprised that he stood right up on his hind legs. There on the bank of the river was the turtle!

"I can't understand how in the world you got here first," cried the rabbit. "How did you do it?"

"By crawling along slowly but surely," said the turtle. "That's the way to win. I may be slow, but I am sure."

The Golden Pears

The Oldest Son's Trip

Once there was a man who had a pear tree that was the joy of his life.

One summer day when the fruit was ripe, the man picked a dozen fine pears and laid them in a basket.

"Take these ripe pears to the king," he said to his oldest son. "They are the finest pears in the whole world. If the king likes them, he'll give you a wonderful present, which you must bring home to me."

273

The two younger sons wanted to go along and see the huge palace, where even the servants were dressed in velvet.

But the father said, "No, your oldest brother is the one to go. He will know how to get a present from the king."

He turned to his oldest son and said, "Take the shortest road to the palace. And don't let anybody steal the pears."

"Oh, they'll be safe with me," said the lad. "I won't let anybody steal them. I'm too clever for that."

Off he went, whistling happily.

After the oldest son had walked for several miles, he came to a field of clover. There he saw a queer old woman taking honey from a beehive.

She had a long nose, sharp eyes, and a pointed chin, and she wore a tall black hat. She looked like a witch, and she was a witch.

"What do you have in your basket, my lad?" she asked in a squeaky voice.

"Just some dirt," said the lad slyly.

"It's dirt, is it?" cried the witch. "Well, my lad with the clever tongue, you'll see if it really is dirt when your trip is ended."

When the lad reached the palace, the servants took him to the throne room. Soon the king came in and sat down on his throne. He wore velvet clothes and had a crown on his head.

The boy went down on his knees and said, "Oh, king, I have brought you some ripe pears, the best in the world."

But when the king uncovered the basket, it was filled with dirt. The witch had made the boy's words come true. She had changed the pears to dirt.

The king threw down the basket of dirt and roared, "Lock this fellow up and keep him locked up."

The Second Son's Trip

For several days the father waited for his oldest son to return. Then he said to his second son, "Take these ripe pears to the king. He will give you golden coins or some other wonderful reward for bringing them."

On his way to the palace the lad saw the old witch with the beehives.

"What is in your basket?" she asked.

The lad felt sure she wanted to steal his pears. So he said, "Just pigs' food."

"Pigs' food!" she cried. "Well, my lad with the clever tongue, you'll see if it's pigs' food when your trip is ended."

Sure enough, when the king uncovered the basket, he found pigs' food. The witch had changed the pears to pigs' food.

"Lock this fellow up," cried the king, "and keep him locked up." So the second son was locked up with his brother.

The Youngest Son's Trip

When the second son did not return, the youngest son said, "Father, let me take a basket of ripe pears to the king's palace. If the king gives me a reward, I'll bring it back, and you'll be rich for the rest of your life."

"You're only a young lad," said the father. "How can you win a reward if your clever brothers had no luck?"

But the lad begged and begged until at last his father said that he might try his luck.

After the lad had walked along for several miles, he came to the clover field. There was the old witch with the long nose and the pointed chin.

"Good day," said the lad pleasantly.

"Good day," said the witch, and she thought, "Here at last is a lad with a friendly tongue in his head."

"You are carrying a heavy load," said
the witch. "What is in your basket?"

"Ripe pears from my father's tree,"
answered the boy politely. "They are the
finest pears in all the world. They are
as yellow as real gold."

"Oho!" said the witch. "So you have
ripe, golden pears. Well, you are a
friendly lad, with a friendly tongue in
your head, and you'll see what is in
your basket when your trip is ended."

The boy said good-by to the old witch
and went off, whistling happily.

He told the servants at the palace that his father had sent a basket of fine, ripe pears to the king.

"Pears!" shouted a servant. "Go away, or we'll lock you up." And he slapped the poor boy.

Another servant slapped him, too, and kicked him and tried to grab his basket.

Just then the princess came out of the palace. She wore a velvet dress, and on her head was a golden crown.

She came forward and spoke to the lad. "What is the matter?" she asked.

The lad went down on his knees and said, "My father sent these ripe pears to the king. But the servants will not let me into the throne room to see him."

"Come with me," said the princess.

The lad followed the princess into the throne room. In a minute the king appeared, looking very fine in velvet clothes and a red and gold crown.

The lad went down on his knees before the king and said, "Oh, king, my father sent you these fine, ripe pears."

This time, when the king uncovered the basket, what should he see but pears of real gold! The witch had changed the pears to golden ones.

"Well, my good lad," said the king, "you shall have a reward." So he gave the boy velvet clothes and gold coins.

Then he sent for the brothers who had been locked up, and set them free. And they all went home to their father with great joy.

A Bell for the Cat

Once upon a time some mice lived in a house that belonged to an old man.

The servants never bothered them. The mice scampered in and out of their holes a dozen times a day. They ran under tables and chairs and chased each other all around the kitchen floor.

In and out of the cupboards they scampered. Nobody bothered to lock or even close the cupboards. So the mice nibbled happily whenever they found a plate of pie or some bits of cheese or some bread crumbs or cookie crumbs.

It was a pleasant life for the mice, until one day a yellow cat came to live in the house. After that everything was different. The mice had an enemy.

If they crept into the kitchen and tried to get into the cupboards, the cat would appear and chase them away.

"We can hardly snatch a crumb of dry bread or a cookie crumb or nibble a bit of cheese," they complained.

It was true. The mice couldn't steal cheese or bread crumbs or cake crumbs. The cat would appear and chase them before they could snatch a single crumb. They knew they would always be hungry unless they got rid of that cat. How they hated her!

The mice kept complaining about their enemy, and finally they decided to make a plan for getting rid of her.

They all got together and sat around in a half circle. But instead of planning, they just kept on complaining.

Finally a fat mouse stepped forward and said, "During all this time you mice have done nothing but complain, while I have thought of a clever plan. It won't get rid of the cat, but it will keep us safe."

"Oho, a plan!" squealed all the other mice. "Tell us about your plan."

Then the fat mouse told them about his plan.

"That wicked cat walks so softly we can't hear her," he said. "Let's fasten a bell around her neck. When she walks, the bell will go ting-a-ling. Then we'll know that she is near, and we can pop into our holes."

"That's a very clever plan!" cried one of the mice. "We'll fasten a bell around the cat's neck, and then we'll all be safe."

A wise old grandfather mouse had been leaning on his stick and thinking. Finally he stepped forward and said, "That's a very clever plan, but somebody must fasten the bell on the cat. Let's decide who will do it."

"Not I! Not I! Not I!" cried several little mice.

The grandfather mouse turned to the fat mouse who had thought of the plan. "Will you promise to fasten the bell on the cat yourself?" he asked.

"Oh, no!" answered the fat mouse.

And no other mouse would promise to fasten the bell on the cat, either.

"Then we must do as we have always done," said the grandfather mouse. "Run when we can, and be caught when we can't. Remember this! It is one thing to talk about a plan, and another thing to make the plan work."

The Fisherman and His Wife

The Wonderful Fish

Long ago a poor fisherman and his wife lived near the sea.

The man caught fish and sold them. That was the way he earned his living. But for weeks he had not sold any fish, because he had not caught any.

Then one day he caught a beautiful golden fish.

"Here's a fine fish!" said the old man. "My wife can cook it for our supper."

But all at once the fish began to speak. "Please throw me back into the sea," it begged. "Please throw me back!"

"I've caught thousands of fish," the man said in great surprise, "but never before have I caught one that talked."

He felt so sorry for the fish that he decided to throw it back into the sea.

When the fish landed on the water, it stood up on its tail. "You shall have a reward for throwing me back," it said. "What would you like?"

The old man stood on the shore and tried to think of something he needed, but he could not think of a single thing.

"Well," said the fish, "if ever you do need something, come to me. I promise that I will give you a reward."

Then the fish dived into the sea.

When the fisherman returned to his hut, he told his wife about the fish.

"It wanted to give me a reward for throwing it back," he said. "But I couldn't think of a thing I needed."

The Loaf of Bread

"I can't understand what you were thinking of," shouted his wife. "We haven't a crumb of bread or a piece of cheese. Our cupboard is empty. Yet you didn't ask for a thing. Go back and ask the fish for a loaf of bread."

The old man knew that his wife would never stop complaining and scolding unless she had her own way. So he went to the edge of the sea and called out,

"Head in air and tail in sea.
Fish, fish, listen to me."

With a great splash of its tail, the golden fish appeared on the water and asked, "What do you want, good man?"

"My wife sent me here to ask for a loaf of bread," said the man. "Our cupboard is empty. We don't have even a loaf of bread or a bit of cheese."

"Go home," said the fish, as it flapped its tail and disappeared into the sea.

"Oh, my," thought the old man, "what a scolding my wife will give me when I come home without a loaf of bread!"

But when he reached home, his wife was all smiles, because a large loaf of bread had appeared in the cupboard.

The New House

The next day the fisherman's wife began to complain again. "A loaf of bread isn't much of a reward," she said. "Go and ask the fish for a new house. This hut is no better than a pig pen."

"I hardly dare to ask for so much," said her husband.

"Well," said the old woman, "if the fish can give us a loaf of bread, it probably can give us a house also."

Once more the old man went to the edge of the sea and called to the fish.

With a splash it appeared.

"My wife sent me here to ask for a new house," said the fisherman. "The roof and the walls of our hut are falling in. My wife says the hut is no better than a pig pen."

"Go home," said the fish, as it flapped its tail and disappeared into the sea.

When the old man returned, he saw a fine new house instead of the hut.

"Welcome, husband," cried his wife. "See what the fish has given us."

She showed him three pretty rooms, with a new table and chairs and all the things they needed.

In the cupboard were beautiful cups and plates and enough food to last for a week.

The fisherman's wife was very happy to have a new house instead of the hut.

The Ragged Wife Becomes a Queen

After two days the fisherman's wife began to complain again.

"This house is not big enough," she said. "I have decided to become a queen and live in a palace. I want to have a gold crown and wear fine clothes of satin and velvet, instead of this ragged dress.

"Husband, go and tell the fish that I have decided to become a queen and live in a palace with many servants."

"Oh, no, wife!" said the husband. "I would not dare to ask for such things."

But his wife sent him down to the edge of the sea. There he called,

"Head in air and tail in sea,
Fish, fish, listen to me."

When the fish appeared, the man told it that his wife wanted to be queen.

"Go home," said the fish, as it flapped its tail and disappeared into the sea.

When the old fisherman returned, he found a palace instead of the house. He crept quietly inside, and there he saw his wife sitting on a golden throne.

She was dressed like a queen, in purple velvet trimmed with gold, and she wore a crown on her head. There were many servants to wait on her.

When she saw her poor husband in his ragged jacket, she screamed, "Away with you! Can't you see that this palace is too fine for a ragged old fisherman?

"Go and stay in the barn and make yourself useful there. A queen can't have a ragged fisherman in her palace."

294

The Fish Disappears

The old man crept away sadly. He hoped his wife would stop complaining, since she had a throne and a palace.

But one day she sent for him, and said, "I have decided to become queen of the waters and have thousands and thousands of fish for my servants. Go and speak to the golden fish about this."

Against his wishes, the old man went down to the edge of the sea and called,

"Head in air and tail in sea,
Fish, fish, listen to me."

Suddenly a fierce storm made huge waves in the sea. The fish appeared, and shouted in an awful voice, "What does your wife want now?"

"She wants to become queen of the waters and have thousands and thousands of fish for servants," said the old man.

The fish did not say a single word.

The storm grew worse and worse. The wind whistled, the thunder roared, and the rain poured down. The sea became dark, and huge waves slapped against the shore.

Then the fish dived to the bottom of the sea, and the storm grew even wilder.

The old fisherman's knees knocked together with fright. He shook with cold in his ragged coat as the wind whistled about him.

On the way home he decided not to tell his wife what had happened. "I'll crawl into the straw and hide," he thought.

But when he reached home, he rubbed his eyes in surprise. The huge palace was gone, the little old hut was back, and there were no servants around.

Inside he found his wife. She was wearing old ragged clothes instead of purple velvet and a crown, but she was singing happily.

Now she was glad to see her husband, even if he was wearing a ragged jacket. They had bread and water for supper, and their plates and cups were cracked, but she never complained at all.

After that the old fisherman and his wife lived happily in their hut near the seashore. And the wife never spoke of her crown and throne.

The husband caught many fish. And sometimes a fish would shine in the sun. Then the man would think of the golden fish, but it never appeared again.

The Princess Who Never Laughed

There was once a beautiful princess who had never laughed in her life. She was always sad.

The king loved his daughter, and he wanted her to laugh and be gay.

At last he sent servants through all the land. They told the people, "Any man who can make the princess laugh shall have her for his wife."

Dozens of young men came to try their luck. They told jokes and did all sorts of tricks. The princess glanced at them now and then, but she never even smiled at their jokes and tricks.

Not far from the king's palace lived a poor lad named Peter, who had often seen the beautiful princess sitting at her window.

As soon as Peter heard of the king's promise, he said to himself, "Maybe I can think of some trick that will make the beautiful princess laugh."

So he decided to try his luck, and off he went to the palace.

When he got there, he did not tell anyone that he had come to make the princess laugh.

Instead, he pretended that he wanted work and begged the cook to let him earn his living by helping her. The cook let him stay and put him to work carrying water and wood.

Every day as the lad worked, he kept watching for a chance to make the princess laugh.

One day, when Peter went to the river to draw some water, he happened to catch a big fish in his pail.

On the way back he met an old woman leading a golden goose by a string.

"That's a fine bird you have," he said.

"No finer than that fish of yours," said the woman. "I'll trade my goose for your fish if you want to trade."

"Well," said Peter, "I might trade."

"If you knew what a wonderful goose it is, you would trade," said the woman. "Everyone who sees the goose stops to pet it. Then if you say some magic words, the people stick fast."

"That goose might be useful to me," said Peter. "Maybe I will trade my fish for it. Tell me the magic words."

The woman said, "The magic words are, 'If you care to come along, hang on.'"

So Peter traded his fish for the goose.

Before long, Peter met a servant girl wearing a yellow cap and apron.

"Let me pet your goose," she said.

"You had better not," said Peter, and he pretended to hurry. "You might pull out some of its golden feathers."

But the servant girl began to pet the goose.

Quick as a wink, Peter said, "If you care to come along, hang on."

How the girl did fight to get loose! She kicked and screamed, but of course she couldn't pull herself free. She had to hang on and go with Peter.

Soon they met the girl's father. When he saw his daughter kicking and fighting to pull herself loose, he took hold of her shoulders and began to pull, too.

"If you care to come along, hang on," shouted Peter.

Of course the man stuck fast to his daughter, who was stuck fast to the golden goose. They kicked, and they screamed, but they couldn't pull loose.

"They have to hang on," thought Peter. "This is a useful bird. It's a treasure! I'm glad I traded my fish for it."

The next one to get stuck was a man playing a fiddle. When Peter said the magic words, the man had to hang on, too. Then a gardener got stuck.

Twice Peter led his queer parade past the window where the princess sat.

She pretended not to notice, but Peter saw her glance out and almost smile.

"Oho!" he thought. "Probably she will laugh soon. I'm very glad that I traded my fish for this goose. It is a real treasure."

He stopped below the window where the princess sat.

During all this time the man kept on playing his fiddle, and people began to come out of the palace and dance in a big circle. As they danced, they sang,

"Heel and toe, heel and toe,
Dancing, dancing, round we go."

The cook rushed out and joined the others. She had come in such a hurry that she carried a big pan, and there was a spot of flour on her nose.

She also began dancing.

"Ha, ha!" cried the gardener, with a loud laugh. "Look at the cook prancing around in her white apron. Doesn't she look silly with that spot of flour on her nose?"

"Silly, am I?" said the cook, giving the gardener a slap.

This was the very chance that Peter wanted. He shouted, "If you care to come along, hang on."

Then the cook stuck fast to the gardener's jacket.

She scolded, kicked, and pulled. How she did fight to get free! But she had to hang on and go where Peter went.

Peter glanced at the princess to see if she was watching the funny sight. She was leaning forward, and Peter noticed a real smile on her face.

"Oho!" he thought. "Now she's going to laugh. She can't help herself."

And for the first time in her life, the beautiful princess did laugh! She opened her mouth wide and laughed so hard that the king had to hold her to keep her from falling.

The king laughed, and Peter laughed. And so did the people who were stuck together. They laughed so hard that they shook all over. And they shook so hard that they all came loose.

Of course the king kept his promise. He gave Peter the princess for his wife, and gave him a crown and a golden throne besides.

And Peter and the beautiful princess lived happily ever after.

Mother Hulda

The Beautiful Daughter

Once upon a time there was a woman who had two daughters.

One of the daughters was as pretty as a picture and worked hard, but the other daughter was ugly and lazy. She did nothing at all.

The beautiful maiden milked the cows, scrubbed the floors, churned the butter, and baked the bread.

But the ugly girl would not churn or bake or scrub or do any work at all. The floors could stay dirty, and the cupboard could be empty, and still she would not work.

One day the beautiful maiden went to the well for a pail of water. She got down on her knees at the edge of the well and leaned over to draw up the heavy pail.

The maiden leaned over so far that she fell head first into the well.

Down she went, down, down, down. The next thing she knew, she was in a beautiful meadow full of red roses and white Easter lilies.

There was a path among the flowers, and she walked along it, wondering where it would lead her.

Soon she came to a queer little house with a high, pointed roof. Just then an old woman popped her head out of the window. When the maiden glanced up and saw an ugly old woman, she started to run away in fright.

But the old woman called to her in a pleasant voice, "Don't be afraid, my dear child. I am Mother Hulda. Come into my house and talk with me."

Mother Hulda looked as ugly as an old troll, but her voice was so kind that the maiden was not frightened any more. She walked into the house.

Then Mother Hulda invited the maiden to live with her. "You may work for me," she said. "And if you are a good helper, I will treat you very kindly. I will treat you as if you were my own daughter."

So the maiden decided to stay with Mother Hulda.

Mother Hulda said, "You must make my bed carefully every day. You must learn to shake the pillows until the feathers are scattered through the air. When you do this, snow falls on the earth."

So the maiden pounded and shook the pillows until the feathers flew around.

"That is right," said Mother Hulda. "Shake the pillows. Make the feathers fly. Then snow will fall on the earth."

The maiden stayed with Mother Hulda and worked hard every day. And Mother Hulda treated her very well. She treated her like a daughter.

One day the maiden said to Mother Hulda, "You have treated me well during my stay here. You have treated me like a daughter, but I miss my mother and sister. Please, may I go back to them?"

"Yes, dear child," said Mother Hulda. "You may go now." And she led the girl to a door, which opened before them.

As the maiden went through the door, a rain of gold coins poured down. The coins stuck to her clothes, so that she was covered with gold from head to toe.

"That is the reward you have earned by helping me," said Mother Hulda.

Then the maiden found herself at the
edge of her mother's yard.

A rooster was on the fence, and when
he saw the maiden all covered with gold
coins, he flapped his wings and crowed,

"Cock-a-doodle-doo, cock-a-doodle-doo.

Your golden girl is back with you."

The maiden said to her mother and
sister, "Mother Hulda treated me very
kindly during my stay. She treated me
like a daughter. And she gave me these
gold coins as a reward for helping
her. You may have them, Mother, and
we'll all live happily together."

The Ugly Daughter

When the lazy girl heard her sister's story, she thought she could probably get some gold, too. She ran straight to the edge of the well and jumped in.

Everything happened just as it had happened to her sister. When the lazy girl opened her eyes, she was in the beautiful meadow, among the roses and Easter lilies.

She hurried down the path, because she could hardly wait to get to the house where Mother Hulda lived.

When the ugly old woman leaned out of the window, the girl didn't feel any fright at all.

Then Mother Hulda invited the lazy girl to stay and work for her.

The girl promised that she would help Mother Hulda, but she was only thinking about the gold coins she would get.

Mother Hulda showed her how to shake the feather pillows, so that snow would fall on the earth.

The first day the ugly girl shook the pillows until the feathers were scattered about, and snow fell on the earth.

The second day she decided that she would not work hard, and she only pretended to shake the pillows.

By the fifth day the lazy girl did not even pretend to work.

Mother Hulda called her, but the girl answered crossly, "I am not going to work. It is foolish to shake those pillows every day, and the house isn't very dirty. I'm going to rest."

Finally Mother Hulda came to the girl's room and said, "Get up, my girl. You are going home today."

This was what the girl wanted to hear. "Now," she thought, "I'll get the gold."

But when Mother Hulda led the girl to the big door, sticky black tar poured over her from head to toe.

"This is your reward for the way you helped me," said Mother Hulda.

The next minute the girl found herself at the edge of her mother's yard.

When the rooster saw the girl with sticky tar all over her, he crowed,

"Cock-a-doodle-doo, cock-a-doodle-doo.
Your tar-black girl is back with you!"

The tar didn't come off the girl until she stopped being lazy. And it was a long time before she learned that lesson.

TO THE TEACHER

Streets and Roads follows *More Friends and Neighbors* and is designed for use during the first half of the third grade. All the words used in the preceding basic books are used in this book. The accompanying *Teacher's Guidebook* and *Think-and-Do Book* (workbook) provide the methodology and materials for a developmental skill-building program in reading at this level.

VOCABULARY LIST

This vocabulary list contains the 419 words introduced in *Streets and Roads*. The following forms of known words are not counted as new: variants formed by adding or dropping the endings *s*, *es*, *d*, *ed*, *ing*, and *er*, *est* of comparison (including those formed by changing *y* to *i* or *f* to *v*, dropping the final *e*, or doubling the final consonant in the root word); possessives; derivatives formed by adding the suffixes *-ly*, *-y*, and *-er* (of agent); compounds made up of two known words; contractions with only one missing letter. Parts of known hyphenated compounds when used as separate words are not counted as new. Homographs are not counted as separate words; for example, if *close* (klōz) has been introduced, *close* (klōs) is not counted as a separate word.

UNIT I	16 rode	29 —	43 —
5 —	sail	30 —	44 bunch
6 automo-	17 closed	31 elevator	bobbing
biles	grove	32 airplanes	45 rent
buses	18 drove	hour	air
7 Hall	19 ahead	33 hundreds	46 —
held	passed	dozens	47 —
8 —	20 —	34 —	48 —
9 half	21 —	35 puzzled	49 —
frighten	22 —	either	50 fancy
10 hurrah	23 seat	36 lady	invited
11 safe	bicycles	37 rushing	51 wearing
we'll	24 wheel	38 Scamp	suit
12 cage	25 awful	monkey	wore
ladder	nobody	39 fifth	52 —
13 felt	stuck	anybody	53 —
mind	26 pounded	40 buttons	54 uncover
14 —	crowd	also	stranger
15 picnic	27 silver	41 purple	55 wrong
eight	28 —	42 I'd	

56 sand-
   wiches
   pieces

57 —
58 jam
   Sarah
   donkey
59 hee-haw
   teacher
60 desks
   drawing
   wasps
61 Don
62 plan
   rid
   sweet
63 hate
   ribbon
   sight
64 carefully
   flapped
65 against
66 —
67 hitched
   they'll
68 true
   fierce
   tiger
69 tickets
   giraffes
   band
70 —
71 gold
72 —
73 drew
74 suppose
   marching
75 dollar
76 —
77 Benny's
   Friday
   toot
78 —
79 chug
80 mistake
81 —

82 breath
   able
   course
83 Tuesday
   buggy
84 spoke
85 feel
   hay
86 tight
   shoulder
87 clapped
88 —
89 ought
   prize
90 Fair
   win
91 fastened
   rang
92 ring
93 belonged
94 —
95 shadow
96 raced
   nine
97 —
98 begin
   pasture
   luck
99 finish
   mile
   eleven
100 nails
   sky
   already
101 circle
   lower
   landed
102 twenty-
   nine
   north
   between
103 —
104 below
105 —
106 son
   raised
107 mine
   rows

108 wall
   fruit
   glasses
109 card
   size
110 sold
   different
111 empty
   load
112 —
113 traveling
   secret
   trimmed
114 gifts
   child
115 Santa
   Claus
   whoa
116 holly
   songs
117 sack
   chocolate
118 —
119 led
   under-
   neath
120 porch
121 jingle
122 —

123 —
124 beaver
   wooden
   jacket
125 farther
126 grumble
127 shakes
128 behave
129 —
130 polite
   welcome
131 Tippy
   naughty
   frisky
132 smash
   pail

133 trunk
   snatched
   peanuts
134 threw
   flat
135 lesson
   shiny
   tin
136 spoiling
   eaten
   lovely
137 —
138 unhappy
139 —
140 Sojo
   idea
   asleep
141 woke
   nap
   yawn
142 begged
   sprinkle
143 moment
144 fellow
145 —
146 evening
147 —
148 limb
   loved
   world
149 owl
   bothered
   hunt
150 tick-tack
   complain
151 dry
   flames
   smoke
152 orange
   spread
   scolding
153 —
154 poured
155 satin
   smooth
   foolish
156 cross
   teeth

317

157 life	182 pillow	207 gnawed	235 slap
158 speak	set	sharp	dived
bottom	183 laid	208 notice	unless
leaped	shade	danger	236 shore
159 frogs	rock	209 crash	fright
croaked	184 lie	free	237 —
160 mud	185 —	210 stirring	238 —
he'll	186 —	probably	239 given
161 worse		211 salt	240 enemy
tears	Unit IV	deer	241 Chuckle
162 —		meadow	whistle
163 logs	187 —	212 pool	242 —
hind	188 Page	fawns	243 clover
164 instead	189 moon	signal	244 flood
165 tar	playmate	213 sneeze	storm
wicked	wink	doe	245 —
166 hid	190 under-	214 block	246 fight
bushes	stand	215 —	during
hit	191 scampered	216 licked	247 —
167 loose	growl	tongues	248 —
168 prancing	chase	217 joy	
enjoying	192 —	218 —	Unit V
ho	193 Fluffytail	219 finally	249 —
169 cook	dare	220 chance	250 lad
roast	194 stone	221 juicy	returned
twisted	guests	222 cups	251 useful
170 —	195 several	plates	worth
171 —	among	grabbed	serve
172 Paddy's	taken	223 thick	252 inn
cabin	196 joined	frosting	cheese
mountain	Lily	fur	253 steal
173 cave	single	224 twice	treasure
grown-up	197 somebody	225 shells	254 coins
poked	198 dashed	226 raccoon	golden
174 berries	199 scattering	227 —	leading
cub	200 —	228 thunder	255 oho
175 paws	201 he'd	popped	thousands
sorts	202 Chip	229 —	rich
176 —	chipmunk	230 apart	256 —
177 —	taught	clam	257 beat
178 —	203 tent	231 stream	crept
179 lean	meal	232 —	258 pretend-
180 mischie-	204 tame	233 —	ing
vous	vacation	234 paddle	259 —
Puckity	bits	twin	260 huge
husband	205 brave	swam	elf
181 steep	206 nibbled		become
cloth	Monday		

318

ILLUSTRATIONS

The pictures in this book were made by Donn P. Crane (pp. 226-239); L. Kate Deal (pp. 15-56); Miriam Story Hurford (pp. 1-2, 58-122); Fiore Mastri (pp. 10, 44-48, 138); Herbert Rudeen (pp. 250-268, 273-281, 287-315); Nell Stolp Smock (pp. 124-179, 269-272, 282-285); Keith Ward (pp. 6-8, 12-13, 188-209); Walter Alois Weber (pp. 211-224, 241-247); and Milo Winter (pp. 180-186).

ACKNOWLEDGMENTS

For permission to adapt and use copyrighted material, grateful acknowledgment is made to the author for "Susan's Birthday Picnic" from "The Hollyberrys and the Hot Day" by A. Dalgliesh; to authors and publishers for "The Big, Long Honk" from "A Great Big Honk" by A. J. Stalson, in *Junior Home for Mothers;* for "Lost and Found" by C. R. Brink, "The Halloween Party" from "The Little Pumpkin Guests" by R. G. Plowhead, "Pinky at the Fair" from "Surprise Performance" by L. R. Davis, "Tippy Elephant's Hat" by J. Norris, and "Paddy's Christmas" by H. A. Monsell, all in *Child Life;* for "Ups and Downs" from "Scamperino's Ups and Downs" by G. King in *Children's Activities;* for "A Funny Balloon Ride" from "Belinda Balloon and the Big Wind" by E. Honness in *The Mayflower;* for "Bread and Jam" from *Ju-Ju and His Friends* by M. van Vrooman: Albert Whitman & Co.; for "A Wish That Came True" from "Circus in Dewberry Lane" by R. G. Plowhead in *Story Parade;* for "Benny's Trick" from "Fuzzy-Wuzz" by M. P. Meigs and "The Story of White Satin" by B. J. Dearborn, both in *Junior Home;* for "Sarah's Plan" from *Sarah's Idea* by Doris Gates, copyright 1938 by Doris Gates and Marjorie Torrey, by permission of The Viking Press, Inc., New York; for "How Tom Went to the Fair" from "The Silver Lining" by E. P. Milbanke in *The Youth's Companion;* for "Peter, Peter, Pumpkin Grower" by F. Bourgeois, copyright 1937, Doubleday, Doran & Company, Inc.; for "The Traveling Christmas Tree" from *Calico* by E. C. Phillips: Houghton Mifflin Company; for "A Ride to Animal Town" by M. C. Potter in *American Childhood;* for "Sojo" by E. Berry: The Harter Publishing Company; for "Noisy Mr. Red Head" adapted from *Martin the Goose Boy* by Marie Barringer, copyright 1932, Doubleday, Doran & Company, Inc., Publishers; for "The Basket of Laughs" from "The Basket of Laughter" in *The Fairies Who Lived in a House* by A. Dalgliesh in *Picture Story Paper*, used by permission of *The Methodist Book Concern;* for "Fluffytail and the Peanut Hunt" from "Fluffytail's Peanut Hunt" by M. H. Comfort in *Boys and Girls:* Whitmore and Smith; for "Chip, the Baby Chipmunk" from "Chipper, the Bold" by E. Hammond in *Wee Wisdom;* for "Salt for the Deer," from "Deer Tamer" by R. J. Canfield in *Jack and Jill;* for "The Bears' Picnic" from "When Three Yellowstone Bears Attended a Picnic" in *Uncle Sam's Animals* by F. M. Fox, copyright 1927 by the Century Co.; for "Ringtail, the Young Raccoon" from *Ringtail* by A. C. Gall and F. H. Crew: Oxford University Press; for "Paddle Tail" from *The Beaver Twins* by J. Tompkins: Frederick A. Stokes Co.; "Chuckle Makes a Friend" from *Chuckle: The Story of a Woodchuck*, by David M. Stearns, copyright, 1939, and reprinted by permission of Farrar & Rinehart, Inc., Publishers; for "The Golden Pears" in *Stories and Story-Telling* by A. M. Keyes: D. Appleton and Company; and for "The Lad Who Went to the North Wind" by G. W. Dasent: G. P. Putnam's Sons.

Acknowledgment is also made to the Harris Estate for "Brother Rabbit and the Tar Baby" from "The Wonderful Tar-Baby Story" by J. C. Harris; and to W. S. Sloan for "Skipper and the Black Dog" from "Shadows" by E. V. Sloan.